LONGMAN IMPRINT BOOKS

Characters from Pre-20th-Century Novels

....

A study collection from the greatest novelists

Selected and edited by Susie Campbell

General editor: Michael Marland
Series consultant: Geoff Barton

LONGMAN

Longman Imprint Books
General editor: Michael Marland

New titles

Previously published titles

Contents

Introduction

The earliest kind of story-telling was in the form of verse or verse-drama. Prose narratives first appeared in the seventeenth century. They were mainly morality tales and allegories. An allegory is a story that has a deeper, spiritual meaning. The people, events and places in the story are symbols. The most famous of these was John Bunyan's *The Pilgrim's Progress*. You can tell that Bunyan's characters are meant to be symbolic from their names: Christian, Faithful, Superstition and Envy, for example.

In the eighteenth century, for the first time, writers started to make up original plots and to create characters who were individuals, not just symbols. Settings became more realistic and detailed and the stories were set in real time rather than the 'once upon a time' of fairy-tales and allegories. For the first time too, characters were given their own individual names, such as Robinson Crusoe, Moll Flanders and Tom Jones. The novel had come into being.

By the end of the eighteenth century, novels had become very popular and there was a big demand for them. One form of novel that became particularly popular at this time was the so-called 'Gothic' novel by writers such as Horace Walpole. Gothic novels were concerned with the supernatural, with mystery and terror. There were a few good ones and very many poor ones. While some people loved them, other people disapproved of them and regarded them as sensationalist.

By the beginning of the nineteenth century, therefore, novels did not have a good reputation. They were seen as light and frivolous, the 'comics' of the day. However, the nineteenth century was the time of some of the most famous English novelists. Writers such as Jane Austen, Charles Dickens and George Eliot persuaded people that novels could be taken seriously.

The spread of education and the greater availability of books due to improvements in printing helped to boost the demand for novels. Many were written in three long volumes and were published as parts of a serial. Instead of watching television, a nineteenth-century family might sit around listening to Father reading aloud the next part of a serialised novel. By the late nineteenth century, more people than ever could read and were demanding readily available fiction. Three-volume novels were replaced by the shorter, cheaper, one-volume novels that we are familiar with today.

As you can see from this brief history, the novel really began with writers taking an interest in individual characters. Right from the beginning of its history, writers have looked for ways in which to make their characters more interesting or more believable. The extracts in this anthology have been arranged chronologically to allow you to see how the techniques of characterisation developed and changed through this period. Because characterisation is such an important aspect of the novel, you will see how the novel itself changed.

Susie Campbell

Journey through Danger

from *The Pilgrim's Progress*

by John Bunyan

Christian has set out on a dangerous journey in order to escape the anger of God. He has many adventures and encounters all sorts of people. These are recounted by Bunyan as though witnessed in a dream. Christian has just passed safely through the first part of the Valley of the Shadow of Death only to realise that the more dangerous part of the journey still lies ahead.

Now morning being come he looked back, not of desire to return, but to see by the light of the day what hazards he had gone through in the dark. So he saw more perfectly the ditch that was on the one hand, and the quag[1] that was on the other; also how narrow the way was which lay betwixt them both; also now he saw the hobgoblins, and satyrs, and dragons of the pit, but all afar off; for after break of day they came not nigh; yet they were discovered to him, according to that which is written, *He discovereth deep things out of darkness, and bringeth out to light the shadow of death.*

Now was Christian much affected with his deliverance from all the dangers of his solitary way, which dangers, though he feared them more before, yet he saw them more clearly now, because the light of the day made them conspicuous to him; and about this time the sun was rising, and this was another mercy to

[1] muddy, marshy ground

Christian: for you must note, that though the first part of the Valley of the Shadow of Death was dangerous, yet this second part which he was yet to go, was, if possible, far more dangerous: for from the place where he now stood, even to the end of the Valley, the way was all along set so full of snares, traps, gins,[2] and nets here, and so full of pits, pitfalls, deep holes, and shelvings down there, that had it now been dark, as it was when he came the first part of the way, had he had a thousand souls, they had in reason been cast away; but, as I said, just now the sun was rising. Then said he '*His candle shineth on my head, and by his light I go through darkness.*'

In this light therefore he came to the end of the Valley. Now I saw in my dream that at the end of this Valley lay blood, bones, ashes, and mangled bodies of men, even of pilgrims that had gone this way formerly: and while I was musing what should be the reason, I espied a little before me a cave, where two giants, Pope and Pagan, dwelt in old time, by whose power and tyranny the men whose bones, blood, ashes, etc., lay there, were cruelly put to death. But by this place Christian went without much danger, whereat I somewhat wondered; but I have learnt since that Pagan has been dead many a day; and as for the other, though he be yet alive he is by reason of age, and also of the many shrewd brushes that he met with in his younger days, grown so crazy and stiff in his joints that he can now do little more than sit in his cave's mouth, grinning at pilgrims as they go by, and biting his nails, because he cannot come at them.

So I saw that Christian went on his way, yet at the sight of the old man that sat in the mouth of the cave, he could not tell what to think, specially because he

[2] traps

spake to him, though he could not go after him, saying, 'You will never mend till more of you be burned': but he held his peace, and set a good face on't, and so went by, and catched no hurt. Then sang Christian,

O world of wonders! (I can say no less)
That I should be preserved in that distress
That I have met with here! O blessed be
That hand that from it hath delivered me!
Dangers in darkness, devils, Hell, and sin,
Did compass me, while I this Vale was in;
Yea, snares, and pits, and traps, and nets did lie
My path about, that worthless silly I
Might have been catched, entangled, and cast down:
But since I live let JESUS *wear the Crown.*

Now as Christian went on his way he came to a little ascent, which was cast up on purpose that pilgrims might see before them: up there therefore Christian went, and looking forward he saw Faithful before him, upon his journey. Then said Christian aloud, 'Ho, ho, so-ho, stay, and I will be your companion.' At that Faithful looked behind him, to whom Christian cried again, 'Stay, stay, till I come up to you'; but Faithful answered, 'No, I am upon my life, and the avenger of blood is behind me.' At this Christian was somewhat moved, and putting to all his strength, he quickly got up with Faithful, and did also over-run him, so the last was first. Then did Christian vain-gloriously[3] smile, because he had gotten the start of his brother: but not taking good heed to his feet, he suddenly stumbled and fell, and could not rise again, until Faithful came up to help him.

Then I saw in my dream they went very lovingly on

[3] proudly

together, and had sweet discourse of all things that had happened to them in their pilgrimage. . . .

Then I saw in my dream that when they were got out of the wilderness they presently saw a town before them, and the name of that town is Vanity; and at the town there is a fair kept called Vanity-Fair. It is kept all the year long; it beareth the name of Vanity-Fair, because the town where 'tis kept is lighter than vanity; and also, because all that is there sold, or that cometh thither, is Vanity. As is the saying of the wise, *All that cometh is vanity.*

This Fair is no new erected business, but a thing of ancient standing; I will show you the original of it.

Almost five thousand years agone, there were pilgrims walking to the Celestial City, as these two honest persons are; and Beelzebub, Apollyon, and Legion, with their companions, perceiving by the path that the Pilgrims made that their way to the City lay through this town of Vanity, they contrived here to set up a fair; a fair wherein should be sold of all sorts of vanity,[4] and that it should last all the year long. Therefore at this Fair are all such merchandise sold, as houses, lands, trades, places, honours, preferments,[5] titles, countries, kingdoms, lusts, pleasures, and delights of all sorts, as whores, bawds, wives, husbands, children, masters, servants, lives, blood, bodies, souls, silver, gold, pearls, precious stones, and what not.

And moreover, at this Fair there is at all times to be seen jugglings, cheats, games, plays, fools, apes, knaves, and rogues, and that of all sorts.

[4] that which is worthless
[5] favours, promotions

Here are to be seen too, and that for nothing, thefts, murders, adulteries, false-swearers, and that of a blood-red colour. . . .

Now these pilgrims, as I said, must needs go through this Fair: well, so they did; but behold, even as they entered into the Fair, all the people in the Fair were moved, and the town itself as it were in a hubbub about them; and that for several reasons: for,

First, the pilgrims were clothed with such kind of raiment as was diverse from the raiment of any that traded in that Fair. The people therefore of the Fair made a great gazing upon them: Some said they were fools, some they were bedlams,[6] and some 'They are outlandish-men.'

Secondly, and as they wondered at their apparel so they did likewise at their speech; for few could understand what they said; they naturally spoke the language of Canaan; but they that kept the Fair, were the men of this world: so that from one end of the Fair to the other, they seemed barbarians each to the other.

Thirdly, but that which did not a little amuse the merchandisers was that these pilgrims set very light by all their wares, they cared not so much as to look upon them; and if they called upon them to buy, they would put their fingers in their ears, and cry, *Turn away mine eyes from beholding vanity*; and look upwards, signifying that their trade and traffic was in Heaven.

One chanced mockingly, beholding the carriages of the men, to say unto them, 'What will ye buy?' but they, looking gravely upon him, said, 'We buy the truth.' At that there was an occasion taken to despise the men the more; some mocking, some taunting, some speaking

[6] madmen

reproachfully, and some calling upon others to smite them. At last things came to an hubbub and great stir in the Fair; insomuch that all order was confounded. Now was word presently brought to the great one of the Fair, who quickly came down and deputed some of his most trusty friends to take these men into examination about whom the Fair was almost overturned. So the men were brought to examination; and they that sat upon them asked them whence they came, whither they went, and what they did there in such an unusual garb? The men told them that they were pilgrims and strangers in the world, and that they were going to their own country, which was the heavenly Jerusalem; and that they had given none occasion to the men of the town, nor yet to the merchandisers, thus to abuse them, and to let them in their journey, except it was for that when one asked them what they would buy, they said they would buy the truth. But they that were appointed to examine them did not believe them to be any other than bedlams and mad, or else such as came to put all things into a confusion in the Fair. Therefore they took them, and beat them, and besmeared them with dirt, and then put them into the cage, that they might be made a spectacle to all the men of the Fair. There therefore they lay for some time, and were made the objects of any man's sport, or malice, or revenge, the great one of the Fair laughing still at all that befell them. But the men being patient, and not rendering railing for railing, but contrariwise blessing, and giving good words for bad, and kindness for injuries done, some men in the Fair that were more observing, and less prejudiced than the rest, began to check and blame the baser sort for their continual abuses done by them to the men. They therefore in angry manner let fly at them again, counting them as bad as the men in the cage, and telling them that they seemed confederates, and should be made partakers of their misfortunes. The other replied that for aught they could see, the men were quiet, and sober, and intended nobody any harm; and that there were many that traded in their Fair that were more worthy to be put into the cage, yea, and pillory[7] too, than were the men that they had abused. Thus, after divers words had passed on both sides (the men behaving themselves all the while very wisely and soberly before them), they fell to some blows among themselves and did harm one to another. Then were these two poor men brought before their examiners again, and there charged as being guilty of the late hubbub that had been in the Fair. So they beat them pitifully, and hanged irons upon them, and led them in chains up and down the Fair, for an example and a terror to others, lest any should further speak in their behalf, or join themselves unto them. But Christian and Faithful behaved themselves yet more wisely, and received the ignominy and shame that was cast upon them with so much meekness and patience, that it won to their side (though but few in comparison of the rest) several of the men in the Fair. This put the other party yet into a greater rage, insomuch that they concluded the death of these two men. Wherefore they threatened that the cage, nor irons, should serve their turn, but that they should die for the abuse they had done and for deluding the men of the Fair.

Then were they remanded to the cage again, until further order should be taken with them. So they put them in, and made their feet fast in the stocks. . . .

[7] place where criminals were fastened by the neck and wrists and exposed to public ridicule

Then a convenient time being appointed, they brought them forth to their trial in order to their condemnation. When the time was come, they were brought before their enemies and arraigned;[8] the Judge's name was Lord Hategood. . . .

The Judge calls on the jury to consider their verdict on Faithful.

Then went the jury out, whose names were Mr Blind-man, Mr No-good, Mr Malice, Mr Love-lust, Mr Live-loose, Mr Heady, Mr High-mind, Mr Enmity, Mr Liar, Mr Cruelty, Mr Hate-light, and Mr Implacable, who every one gave in his private verdict against him among themselves, and afterwards unanimously concluded to bring him in guilty before the Judge. And first Mr Blind-man, the foreman, said, 'I see clearly that this man is an heretic.' Then said Mr No-good, 'Away with such a fellow from the earth.' 'Ay,' said Mr Malice, 'for I hate the very looks of him.' Then said Mr Love-lust, 'I could never endure him.' 'Nor I,' said Mr Live-loose, 'for he would always be condemning my way.' 'Hang him, hang him,' said Mr Heady. 'A sorry scrub,' said Mr High-mind. 'My heart riseth against him,' said Mr Enmity. 'He is a rogue,' said Mr Liar. 'Hanging is too good for him,' said Mr Cruelty. 'Let's dispatch him out of the way,' said Mr Hate-light. Then said Mr Implacable, 'Might I have all the world given me, I could not be reconciled to him, therefore let us forthwith bring him in guilty of death.' And so they did, therefore he was presently condemned to be had from the place where he was, to the place from whence he came, and there to be put to the most

[8] accused

cruel death that could be invented.

They therefore brought him out to do with him according to their law; and first they scourged him, then they buffeted him, then they lanced his flesh with knives; after that they stoned him with stones, then pricked him with their swords; and last of all they burned him to ashes at the stake. Thus came Faithful to his end. Now, I saw that there stood behind the multitude a chariot and a couple of horses, waiting for Faithful, who (so soon as his adversaries had dispatched him) was taken up into it, and straightway was carried up through the clouds, with sound of trumpet, the nearest way to the Celestial Gate. But as for Christian, he had some respite, and was remanded back to prison; so he there remained for a space: but he that over-rules all things, having the power of their rage in his own hand, so wrought it about that Christian for that time escaped them, and went his way.

And as he went he sang.

Well Faithful, thou hast faithfully professed
Unto thy Lord: with him thou shalt be blest;
When faithless ones with all their vain delights
Are crying out under their hellish plights,
Sing, Faithful, sing, and let thy name survive,
For though they killed thee, thou art yet alive.

Shipwrecked

from *Robinson Crusoe*

by Daniel Defoe

Robinson Crusoe has been shipwrecked on a desert island. He is the only survivor of a terrible storm that drove his ship on to a sandbank. He manages to swim ashore, where he spends an uncomfortable night sleeping in the branches of a tree. The next morning, he sets about the business of survival.

When I waked it was broad day, the weather clear, and the storm abated, so that the sea did not rage and swell as before: but that which surprised me most was that the ship was lifted off in the night from the sand where she lay, by the swelling of the tyde, and was driven up almost as far as the rock which I first mentioned, where I had been so bruised by the dashing me against it; this being within about a mile from the shore where I was, and the ship seeming to stand upright still, I wished my self on board, that, at least, I might save some necessary things for my use.

When I came down from my apartment in the tree, I looked about me again, and the first thing I found was the boat, which lay as the wind and the sea had tossed her up upon the land, about two miles on my right hand. I walked as far as I could upon the shore to have got to her, but found a neck or inlet of water between me and the boat, which was about half a mile broad, so I came back for the present, being more intent upon getting at the ship, where I hoped to find something for my present subsistence.

A little after noon I found the sea very calm, and the tyde ebbed so far out that I could come within a quarter of a mile of the ship; and here I found a fresh renewing of my grief, for I saw evidently, that if we had kept on board, we had been all safe, that is to say, we had all got safe on shore, and I had not been so miserable as to be left entirely destitute of all comfort and company, as I now was; this forced tears from my eyes again, but as there was little relief in that, I resolved, if possible, to get to the ship, so I pulled off my clothes, for the weather was hot to extremity, and took the water, but when I came to the ship, my difficulty was still greater to know how to get on board, for as she lay a ground, and high out of the water, there was nothing within my reach to lay hold of. I swam round her twice, and the second time I spy'd a small piece of a rope, which I wondered I did not see at first, hang down by the fore-chains so low, as that with great difficulty I got hold of it, and by the help of that rope, got up into the forecastle of the ship. Here I found that the ship was bulged, and had a great deal of water in her hold, but that she lay so on the side of a bank of hard sand, or rather earth, that her stern lay lifted up upon the bank, and her head low almost to the water; by this means all her quarter was free, and all that was in that part was dry; for you may be sure my first work was to search and to see what was spoiled and what was free; and first I found that all the ship's provisions were dry and untouched by the water, and being very well disposed to eat, I went to the bread-room and filled my pockets with bisket, and eat it as I went about other things, for I had no time to lose; I also found some rum in the great cabbin, of which I took a large dram, and which I had indeed need enough of to spirit me for what was before me. Now I wanted nothing but a boat to furnish my self with many things which I foresaw would be very necessary to me. . . .

Robinson builds himself a raft.

My raft was now strong enough to bear any reasonable weight; my next care was what to load it with, and how to preserve what I laid upon it from the surf of the sea, but I was not long considering this. I first laid all the planks or boards upon it that I could get, and having considered well what I most wanted, I first got three of the seamen's chests, which I had broken open and empty'd, and lowered them down upon my raft; the first of these I filled with provision, viz. bread, rice, three Dutch cheeses, five pieces of dry'd goat's flesh, which we lived much upon, and a little remainder of European corn which had been laid by for some fowls which we brought to sea with us, but the fowls were killed; there had been some barly and wheat together, but, to my great disappointment, I found afterwards that the rats had eaten or spoiled it all; as for liquors, I found several cases of bottles belonging to our skipper, in which were some cordial waters, and in all about five or six gallons of rack; these I stowed by themselves, there being no need to put them into the chest, nor no room for them. While I was doing this, I found the tyde began to flow, tho' very calm, and I had the mortification to see my coat, shirt, and wastcoat which I had left on shore upon the sand, swim away; as for my breeches, which were only linnen and open knee'd, I swam on board in them and my stockings. However, this put me upon rummaging for clothes, of which I found enough, but took no more than I wanted for present use, for I had other things which my eye was more upon, as first tools to work with on shore, and it was after long searching that I found out the carpenter's chest, which was indeed a very useful prize to me, and much more valuable than a ship loading of gold would have been at that time; I got it down to my raft, even whole as it was, without losing time to look into it, for I knew in general what it contained.

My next care was for some ammunition and arms; there were two very good fowling-pieces in the great cabbin, and two pistols; these I secured first, with some powder-horns,[1] and a small bag of shot, and two old rusty swords; I knew there were three barrels of powder in the ship, but knew not where our gunner had stowed them, but with much search I found them, two of them dry and good, the third had taken water; those two I got to my raft, with the arms; and now I thought my self pretty well freighted, and began to think how I should get to shore with them, having neither sail, oar, or rudder, and the least cap full of wind would have overset all my navigation.

I had three encouragements: 1. a smooth calm sea; 2. the tide rising, and setting in to the shore; 3. what little wind there was blew me towards the land; and thus, having found two or three broken oars belonging to the boat, and besides the tools which were in the chest, I found two saws, an axe, and a hammer, and with this cargo I put to sea. For a mile, or thereabouts, my raft went very well, only that I found it drive a little distant from the place where I had landed before, by which I perceived that there was some indraft of the water, and consequently I hoped to find some creek or river there, which I might make use of as a port to get to land with my cargo.

As I imagined, so it was, there appeared before me a

[1] flasks for carrying gunpowder

little opening of the land, and I found a strong current of the tide set into it, so I guided my raft as well as I could to keep in the middle of the stream. But here I had like to have suffered a second shipwreck, which, if I had, I think verily would have broke my heart, for knowing nothing of the coast, my raft run a-ground at one end of it upon a shoal, and not being a-ground at the other end, it wanted but a little that all my cargo had slip'd off towards that end that was a-float, and so fallen into the water. I did my utmost by setting my back against the chests to keep them in their places, but could not thrust off the raft with all my strength, neither durst I stir from the posture I was in, but holding up the chests with all my might, stood in that manner near half an hour, in which time the rising of the water brought me a little more upon a level, and a little after, the water still rising, my raft floated again, and I thrust her off with the oar I had into the channel, and then driving up higher, I at length found my self in the mouth of a little river, with land on both sides, and a strong current or tide running up. I looked on both sides for a proper place to get to shore, for I was not willing to be driven too high up the river, hoping in time to see some ship at sea, and therefore resolved to place my self as near the coast as I could.

At length I spy'd a little cove on the right shore of the creek, to which with great pain and difficulty I guided my raft, and at last got so near, as that, reaching ground with my oar, I could thrust her directly in; but here I had like to have dipt all my cargo in the sea again; for that shore lying pretty steep, that is to say sloping, there was no place to land but where one end of my float, if it run on shore, would lie so high, and the other sink lower as before, that it would endanger my cargo again. All that I could do was to wait 'till the tide was at the highest, keeping the raft with my oar like an anchor to hold the side of it fast to the shore, near a flat piece of ground, which I expected the water would flow over; and so it did. As soon as I found water enough, for my raft drew about a foot [of] water, I thrust her on upon that flat piece of ground, and there fastened or mored her by sticking my two broken oars into the ground, one on one side near one end, and one on the other side near the other end; and thus I lay 'till the water ebbed away, and left my raft and all my cargoe safe on shore.

My next work was to view the country, and seek a proper place for my habitation, and where to stow my goods to secure them from whatever might happen; where I was, I yet knew not, whether on the continent or on an island, whether inhabited or not inhabited, whether in danger of wild beasts or not. There was a hill not above a mile from me, which rose up very steep and high, and which seemed to over-top some other hills, which lay as in a ridge from it northward; I took out one of the fowling pieces, and one of the pistols, and an horn of powder, and thus armed I travelled for discovery up to the top of that hill, where after I had with great labour and difficulty got to the top, I saw my fate to my great affliction, viz. that I was in an island environed every way with the sea, no land to be seen, except some rocks which lay a great way off, and two small islands less than this, which lay about three leagues to the west. . . .

After exploring the island, Robinson makes a second trip to the ship.

I was under some apprehensions during my absence from the land, that at least my provisions might be devoured on shore; but when I came back, I found no sign of any visitor, only there sat a creature like a wild cat upon one of the chests, which when I came towards it, ran away a little distance, and then stood still; she sat very composed and unconcerned, and looked full in my face, as if she had a mind to be acquainted with me. I presented my gun at her, but as she did not understand it, she was perfectly unconcerned at it, nor did she offer to stir away; upon which I tossed her a bit of bisket, tho' by the way I was not very free of it, for my store was not great. However, I spared her a bit, I say, and she went to it, smelled of it, and ate it, and looked (as pleased) for more, but I thanked her, and could spare no more, so she marched off.

Having got my second cargoe on shore, tho' I was fain to open the barrels of powder and bring them by parcels, for they were too heavy, being large casks, I went to work to make me a little tent with the sail and some poles which I cut for that purpose, and into this tent I brought every thing that I knew would spoil, either with rain or sun, and I piled all the empty chests and casks up in a circle round the tent, to fortify it from any sudden attempt, either from man or beast.

When I had done this I blocked up the door of the tent with some boards within, and an empty chest set up on end without, and spreading one of the beds upon the ground, laying my two pistols just at my head, and my gun at length by me, I went to bed for the first time, and slept very quietly all night, for I was very weary and heavy, for the night before I had slept little, and had laboured very hard all day, as well to fetch all those things from the ship, as to get them on shore.

A Desperate Escape

from *Pamela*

by Samuel Richardson

Pamela is a virtuous young serving-maid who shows great
spirit in defying the dishonourable intentions of her mistress's
son, Mr B. She tells her story in a series of letters to her
parents. In this extract, she writes about her attempt to escape
from the clutches of her would-be seducer when he leaves her
in the care of the evil Mrs Jewkes and Monsieur Colbrand.

I took with me but one shift, besides what I had on, and
two handkerchiefs, and two caps, which my pocket held
(for it was not for me to encumber myself), and all my
stock of money, which was but five or six shillings, to
set out for I knew not whither; and got out of the
window, not without some difficulty, sticking a little at
my shoulders and hips; but I was resolved to get out, if
possible. The distance from the window to the leads[1]
was greater than I had imagined, and I was afraid I had
sprained my ancle; and the distance from the leads to
the ground, was still greater; but I got no hurt considerable enough to hinder me from pursuing my
intentions. So, being now in the garden, I hid my
papers under a rose-bush, and covered them over
with mould,[2] and there I hope they still lie. Then I hied
away to the pond: the clock struck twelve, just as I
got out; and it was a dark misty night, and very cold;

[1] the roof
[2] loose earth

but I was not then sensible of it.

When I came to the pond-side I flung in my upper coat, as I had designed, and my handkerchief, and round-eared cap, with a knot[3] pinned upon it; and then ran to the door, and took the key out of my pocket, my poor heart beating all the time, as if it would have forced its way through my stays.[4] But how miserably was I disappointed, when I found that my key would not open the lock! The wretch, as it proved, had taken off the old lock, and another was put on! I tried and tried before I was convinced it was so; but feeling about found a padlock on another part of the door; then how my heart sunk! I dropped down with grief and confusion, unable to stir for a while. But my terror soon awakened my resolution; for I knew that my attempt, if I escaped not, would be sufficient to give a pretence for the most outrageous insults from the woman; and for the cruelest treatment from my master; and to bring him down the sooner to put his horrid purposes in execution; I therefore was resolved, if possible, to get over the wall; but that being high, had no other hope to do it, than by help of the ledges of the door, which are very strong and thick. I clambered up, therefore, upon them, and upon the lock, which was a great wooden one; and reached the top of the door with my hands; which shut not close to the wall; and then, little thinking I could climb so well, I made shift to lay hold on the top of the wall with my hands: but, alas for me! nothing but ill luck! no escape for poor Pamela! The wall being old, the bricks I held by, gave way, just as I was taking a spring to get up; and down came I, and received such a blow upon my head, with one of the

---

[3] knot of ribbon
[4] corset

bricks, that it quite stunned me; and I broke my shins and my ancle besides, and beat off the heel of one of my shoes.

In this dreadful way, flat upon the ground, I lay, for I believe five or six minutes; and then trying to get up, I sunk down again two or three times. My left hip and shoulder were sadly bruised, and pained me much; and besides my head bled quite down into my neck, as I could feel, and aked grievously with the blow I had with the brick. Yet these hurts I valued not; but crept a good way upon my knees and hands, in search of a ladder I just recollected to have seen against the wall two days before, on which the gardener was nailing a nectarine branch, that was loosened from the wall: but no ladder could I find. What, now, thought I, must become of the miserable Pamela! Then I began to wish myself again in my closet,[5] and to repent of my attempt, which I now censured as rash; but that was because it did not succeed.

God forgive me! but a sad thought came just then into my head! I tremble to think of it! Indeed my apprehensions of the usage I should meet with, had like to have made me miserable for ever! O my dear, dear parents, forgive your poor child! But being then quite desperate, I crept along, till I could raise myself on my staggering feet; and away limped I! What to do, but to throw myself into the pond, and so put a period to all my terrors in this world! But, oh! to find them infinitely aggravated in a miserable *eternity*! had I not by the *Divine Grace* been with-held. . . .

It was well for me, as I have since thought, that I was so bruised as I was; for this made me the longer before I

---

[5] bedroom

got to the water; and gave time for a little reflection, for a ray of grace to dart in upon my benighted mind; and so, when I came to the pond-side, I sat myself down on the sloping bank, and began to ponder my wretched condition; and thus I reasoned with myself:

Pause here a little, Pamela, on what thou art about, before thou takest the dreadful leap; and consider whether there be no way yet left, no hope, if not to escape from this wicked house, yet from the mischiefs threatened thee in it!

I then cosidered, and after I had cast about in my mind, every thing that could make me hope, and saw no probability; a wicked woman, devoid of all compassion! a horrid abetter just arrived in this dreadful Colbrand! an angry and resenting master, who now hated me, and threatened me with the most dreadful evils! and that I should, in all probability, be soon deprived even of the opportunity I now had before me, to free myself from all their persecutions! What hast thou to do, distressed creature, *said I to myself*, but to throw thyself upon a merciful God (who knows how innocently thou sufferest), to avoid the merciless wickedness of those who are determined on thy ruin?

And then, thought I (and O that thought was surely of the devil's instigation; for it was very soothing and powerful with me) these wicked wretches, who now have no remorse, no pity on me, will then be moved to lament their misdoings; and when they see the dead corpse of the miserable Pamela dragged out to these dewy banks, and lying breathless at their feet, they will find that remorse to soften their obdurate hearts, which, now, has no place in them! And my master, my angry master, will then forget his resentments, and say, 'Alas!' and it may be, wring his hands. 'This is the

unhappy Pamela! whom I have so causelessly persecuted and destroyed! Now do I see she preferred her
honesty to her life. She, poor girl! was no hypocrite, no
deceiver; but really was the innocent creature she
pretended to be!'

Then, thought I, will he, perhaps, shed a few tears
over the corpse of his persecuted servant; and, though
he may give out, it was disappointment, and (in order
to hide his own guilt) love for poor Mr Williams;[6] yet
will he be inwardly grieved, and order me a decent
funeral, and save me, or rather *this part* of me, from the
dreadful stake, and the highway interment: and the
young men and maidens in my father's neighbourhood
will pity poor Pamela! But yet I hope I shall not be the
subject of their ballads and their elegies, but that my
memory, for the sake of my dear father and mother,
may quickly slide into oblivion!

I was once rising, so indulgent was I to this sad way of
thinking, to throw myself in: but again my bruises made
me slow; and I thought, What art thou about to do,
wretched Pamela? How knowest thou, though the
prospect be all dark to thy short-sighted eye, what God
may do for thee, even when all human means fail? God
Almighty would not lay me under these sore afflictions,
if he had not given me strength to grapple with
them . . .

And so saying, I arose; but was so stiff with my hurts,
so cold with the dew of the night, and the wet grass on
which I had sat, as also with the damps arising from so
large a piece of water, that with great pain I got from
this pond, which now I think of with terror; and
bending my limping steps towards the house, took

6 the chaplain, who is Pamela's friend

refuge in the corner of an out-house, where wood and coals are laid up for family use: there, behind a pile of fire-wood, I crept, and lay down, as you may imagine, with a heart just broken; expecting to be soon found out by cruel keepers, and to be worse treated than ever I yet had been.

This, my dear father and mother, is the issue of your poor Pamela's fruitless enterprize; and who knows, if I had got out at the back-door, whether I had been at all in a better case, moneyless, friendless, as I am, and in a strange place! But blame not your poor daughter too much: nay, if ever you see this miserable scribble, all bathed and blotted with my tears, let your pity get the better of your reprehension! But I know it will.

I must leave off for the present; for my strength and my will are at this time far unequal to each other. But yet I will add, that though I should have praised God for my deliverance, had I been freed from my wicked keepers, and my designing master; yet I have more abundant reason to praise him, that I have been delivered from a worse enemy – *Myself!*

I will continue my sad relation.

It seems Mrs Jewkes awaked not till day-break; and not finding me in bed, she called out for me; and no answer being returned, arose and ran to my closet. Finding me not there, she searched under the bed, and in another closet; having before examined the chamber-door, and found it as she had left it, quite fast, and the key, as usual, about her wrist. For if I could have stole that from her, in her dead sleep, and got out at the chamber-door, there were two or three passages, and doors to them all, double-locked and barred, to go through, into the great garden; so that there was no way to escape, but out of the window; and of that window I dropped from, because of the summer parlour under it; the other windows being a great way from the ground.

She says, she was excessively alarmed. She instantly raised the two maids, who lay not far off, and then the Swiss; and finding every door fast, she said, I must be carried away, as St Peter was, out of prison, by some angel. It is a wonder she had not a worse thought.

She says, she wept, wrung her hands, and ran about like a mad woman, little thinking I could have got out of the closet-window, between the iron bars; and indeed I don't know whether I could do so again. But at last, finding that casement open, they concluded it must be so; and ran out into the garden, and found my footsteps in the mould of the bed which I dropped down upon from the leads: and so speeded away all of them, that is to say, Mrs Jewkes, Colbrand, Nan, and the gardener, who by that time had joined them, towards the back door, to see if that was fast, while the cook was sent to the out-offices to raise the men-servants, and make them get horses ready, to take each a several way to pursue me.

But it seems, finding that door double-locked and padlocked, and the heel of my shoe, and the broken bricks, they verily concluded I was got away by some means over the wall; and then, they say, Mrs Jewkes seemed like a distracted woman: till at last Nan had the thought to go towards the pond, and there seeing my coat, and cap and handkerchief, in the water, cast almost to the banks by the motion of the waves, she thought it was me, and screaming out, ran to Mrs Jewkes, and said, 'O madam, madam! here's a piteous thing! Mrs Pamela lies drowned in the pond!'

Thither they all ran; and finding my clothes, doubted

not but I was at the bottom; and then they all, Swiss among the rest, beat their breasts, and made most dismal lamentations; and Mrs Jewkes sent Nan to the men, to bid them get the drag-net ready, and leave the horses, and come to try to find the poor innocent, as she, it seems, *then* called me, beating her breast, and lamenting my hard hap; but most what would become of them, and what account they should give to my master.

While every one was thus differently employed, some weeping and wailing, some running here and there, Nan came into the wood-house; and there lay poor I, so weak, so low, and so dejected, and withal so stiff with my bruises, that I could not stir nor help myself to get upon my feet. And I said, with a low voice (for I could hardly speak), 'Mrs Ann, Mrs Ann!' The creature was sadly frighted, but was taking up a billet to knock me on the head, believing I was some thief, as she said; but I cried out, 'O Mrs Ann, Mrs Ann! help me, for pity's sake, to Mrs Jewkes! for I cannot get up.' 'Bless me!' said she, 'what! you, madam! Why our hearts are almost broken, and we were going to drag the pond for you, believing you had drowned yourself. Now,' said she, 'shall we be all alive again!'

Without staying to help me, she ran away to the pond, and brought all the crew to the wood-house. The wicked woman, as she entered, said, 'Where is she? Plague of her spells, and her witch-crafts! She shall dearly repent of this trick, if my name be Jewkes'; and coming to me, took hold of my arm so roughly, and gave me such a pull, as made me scream out (my shoulder being bruised on that side), and drew me on my face. 'O cruel creature!' said I, 'if you knew what I have suffered, it would move you to pity me!'

Even Colbrand seemed to be concerned, and said,

'Fie, madam, fie! you see she is almost dead! You must not be so rough with her.' The coachman Robin seemed to be sorry for me too, and said, with sobs, 'What a scene is here! Don't you see she is all bloody in her head, and cannot stir?' 'Curse of her contrivances!' said the horrid creature; 'she has frightened *me* out of my wits, I'm sure. How the d—I came you here?' 'O,' said I, 'ask me now no questions, but let the maids carry me up to my prison; and there let me die decently, and in peace!' Indeed I thought I could not live two hours.

'I suppose,' said the tygress, 'you want Mr Williams to pray by you, don't you? Well, I'll send for my master this minute! Let him come and watch you himself, for me; for there's no such thing as a woman's holding you, I'm sure.'

The maids took me up between them, and carried me to my chamber; and when the wretch saw how bad I was, she began a little to relent.

I was so weak, that I fainted away, as soon as they got me up stairs; and they undressed me, and got me to-bed, and Mrs Jewkes ordered Nan to bathe my shoulder, and arm, and ancle, with some old rum warmed; and they cut from the back part of my head, a little of the hair, for it was clotted with blood; and put a family plaster to the gash, which was pretty long, but not deep. If this woman has any good quality, it is, it seems, in a readiness and skill to manage in cases where sudden accidents happen in a family.

After this, I fell into a pretty sound and refreshing sleep, and lay till near twelve o'clock, tolerably easy, yet was feverish, and anguishly inclined. The wretch took a great deal of care of me: but for what end? Why, to fit me to undergo more troubles; for that is the sad case.

A Family Row

from *Tom Jones*

by Henry Fielding

Sophia Western has fallen in love with Tom Jones, who has just been thrown out of the house where he was brought up. Her father and her aunt want her to marry Mr Blifil.

The morning in which Mr Jones departed, Mrs Western summoned Sophia into her apartment; and having first acquainted her that she had obtained her liberty of her father, she proceeded to read her a long lecture on the subject of matrimony; which she treated not as a romantic scheme of happiness arising from love, as it hath been described by the poets; nor did she mention any of those purposes for which we are taught by divines[1] to regard it as instituted by sacred authority; she considered it rather as a fund in which prudent women deposit their fortunes to the best advantage, in order to receive a larger interest for them than they could have elsewhere.

When Mrs Western had finished, Sophia answered, 'That she was very incapable of arguing with a lady of her aunt's superior knowledge and experience, especially on a subject which she had so very little considered, as this of matrimony.'

'Argue with me, child!' replied the other; 'I do not indeed expect it. I should have seen the world to very little purpose truly, if I am to argue with one of your

[1] priests

years. I have taken this trouble, in order to instruct you. The antient philosophers, such as Socrates, Alcibiades, and others, did not use to argue with their scholars. You are to consider me, child, as Socrates, not asking your opinion, but only informing you of mine.' From which last words the reader may possibly imagine, that this lady had read no more of the philosophy of Socrates, than she had of that of Alcibiades; and indeed we cannot resolve his curiosity as to this point.

'Madam,' cries Sophia, 'I have never presumed to controvert[2] any opinion of yours; and this subject, as I said, I have never yet thought of, and perhaps never may.'

'Indeed, Sophy,' replied the aunt, 'this dissimulation with me is very foolish. The French shall as soon persuade me that they take foreign towns in defence only of their own country, as you can impose on me to believe you have never yet thought seriously of matrimony. How can you, child, affect to deny that you have considered of contracting an alliance, when you so well know I am acquainted with the party with whom you desire to contract it? – an alliance as unnatural, and contrary to your interest, as a separate league with the French would be to the interest of the Dutch! But however, if you have not hitherto considered of this matter, I promise you it is now high time, for my brother is resolved immediately to conclude the treaty with Mr Blifil; and indeed I am a sort of guarantee in the affair, and have promised your concurrence.'

'Indeed; madam,' cries Sophia, 'this is the only instance in which I must disobey both yourself and my father. For this is a match which requires very little consideration in me to refuse.'

[2] contradict

'If I was not as great a philosopher as Socrates himself,' returned Mrs Western, 'you would overcome my patience. What objection can you have to the young gentleman?'

'A very solid objection, in my opinion,' says Sophia – 'I hate him.'

'Will you never learn a proper use of words?' answered the aunt. 'Indeed, child, you should consult Bailey's Dictionary. It is impossible you should hate a man from whom you have received no injury. By hatred, therefore, you mean no more than dislike, which is no sufficient objection against your marrying of him. I have known many couples, who have entirely disliked each other, lead very comfortable genteel lives. Believe me, child, I know these things better than you. You will allow me, I think, to have seen the world, in which I have not an acquaintance who would not rather be thought to dislike her husband than to like him. The contrary is such out-of-fashion romantic nonsense, that the very imagination of it is shocking.'

'Indeed, madam,' replied Sophia, 'I shall never marry a man I dislike. If I promise my father never to consent to any marriage contrary to his inclinations, I think I may hope he will never force me into that state contrary to my own.'

'Inclinations!' cries the aunt, with some warmth. 'Inclinations! I am astonished at your assurance. A young woman of your age, and unmarried, to talk of inclinations! But whatever your inclinations may be, my brother is resolved; nay, since you talk of inclinations, I shall advise him to hasten the treaty. Inclinations!'

Sophia then flung herself upon her knees, and tears began to trickle from her shining eyes. She entreated her aunt, 'to have mercy upon her, and not to resent so cruelly her unwillingness to make herself miserable;'

often urging, 'that she alone was concerned, and that her happiness only was at stake.'

As a bailiff, when well authorized by his writ, having possessed himself of the person of some unhappy debtor, views all his tears without concern; in vain the wretched captive attempts to raise compassion; in vain the tender wife bereft of her companion, the little prattling boy, or frighted girl, are mentioned as inducements to reluctance. The noble bumtrap, blind and deaf to every circumstance of distress, greatly rises above all the motives to humanity, and into the hands of the gaoler resolves to deliver his miserable prey.

Not less blind to the tears, or less deaf to every entreaty of Sophia was the politic aunt, nor less determined was she to deliver over the trembling maid into the arms of the gaoler Blifil. She answered with great impetuosity, 'So far, madam, from your being concerned alone, your concern is the least, or surely the least important. It is the honour of your family which is concerned in this alliance; you are only the instrument. Do you conceive, mistress, that in an intermarriage between kingdoms, as when a daughter of France is married into Spain, the princess herself is alone considered in the match? No! it is a match between two kingdoms, rather than between two persons. The same happens in great families such as ours. The alliance between the families is the principal matter. You ought to have a greater regard for the honour of your family than for your own person; and if the example of a princess cannot inspire you with these noble thoughts, you cannot surely complain at being used no worse than all princesses are used.'

'I hope, madam,' cries Sophia, with a little elevation of voice, 'I shall never do anything to dishonour my family; but as for Mr Blifil, whatever may be the consequence, I am resolved against him, and no force shall prevail in his favour.'

Western, who had been within hearing during the greater part of the preceding dialogue, had now exhausted all his patience; be therefore entered the room in a violent passion, crying, 'D—n me then if shatunt ha'un, d—n me if shatunt, that's all – that's all; d—n me if shatunt.'

Mrs Western had collected a sufficient quantity of wrath for the use of Sophia; but she now transferred it all to the squire. 'Brother,' said she, 'it is astonishing that you will interfere in a matter which you had totally left to my negotiation. Regard to my family hath made me take upon myself to be the mediating power, in order to rectify those mistakes in policy which you have committed in your daughter's education. For, brother, it is you – it is your preposterous conduct which hath eradicated all the seeds that I had formerly sown in her tender mind. It is you yourself who have taught her disobedience.' – 'Blood!' cries the squire, foaming at the mouth, 'you are enough to conquer the patience of the devil! Have I ever taught my daughter disobedience? – Here she stands; speak honestly, girl, did ever I bid you be disobedient to me? Have not I done everything to humour and to gratify you, and to make you obedient to me? And very obedient to me she was when a little child, before you took her in hand and spoiled her, by filling her head with a pack of court notions. Why – why – why – did I not overhear you telling her she must behave like a princess? You have made a Whig[3] of the girl; and how should her father, or anybody else, expect any obedience from her?' – 'Brother,' answered Mrs Western, with an air of great

[3] radical politician

disdain, 'I cannot express the contempt I have for your politics of all kinds; but I will appeal likewise to the young lady herself, whether I have ever taught her any principles of disobedience. On the contrary, niece, have I not endeavoured to inspire you with a true idea of the several relations in which a human creature stands in society? Have I not taken infinite pains to show you, that the law of nature hath enjoined a duty on children to their parents? Have I not told you what Plato says on that subject? – a subject on which you was so notoriously ignorant when you came first under my care, that I verily believe you did not know the relation between a daughter and a father.' – ''Tis a lie,' answered Western. 'The girl is no such fool, as to live to eleven years old without knowing that she was her father's relation.' – 'O! more than Gothic[4] ignorance,' answered the lady. 'And as for your manners, brother, I must tell you, they deserve a cane.' – 'Why then you may gi' it me, if you think you are able,' cries the squire; 'nay, I suppose your niece there will be ready enough to help you.' – 'Brother,' said Mrs Western, 'though I despise you beyond expression, yet I shall endure your insolence no longer; so I desire my coach may be got ready immediately, for I am resolved to leave your house this very morning.' – 'And a good riddance too,' answered he; 'I can bear your insolence no longer, as you come to that. Blood! it is almost enough of itself to make my daughter undervalue my sense, when she hears you telling me every minute you despise me.' – 'It is impossible, it is impossible,' cries the aunt; 'no one can undervalue such a boor.' – 'Boar,' answered the squire, 'I am no boar; no, nor ass; no, nor rat neither, madam. Remember that – I am no rat. I am a true

4 old and barbaric

Englishman, and not of your Hanover breed,[5] that have eat up the nation.' – 'Thou art one of those wise men,' cries she, 'whose nonsensical principles have undone the nation; by weakening the hands of our government at home, and by discouraging our friends and encouraging our enemies abroad.' – 'Ho! are you come back to your politics?' cries the squire: 'as for those I despise them as much as I do a f—t.' Which last words he accompanied and graced with the very action, which, of all others, was the most proper to it. And whether it was this word or the contempt exprest for her politics, which most affected Mrs Western, I will not determine; but she flew into the most violent rage, uttered phrases improper to be here related, and instantly burst out of the house. Nor did her brother or her niece think proper either to stop or to follow her; for the one was so much possessed by concern, and the other by anger, that they were rendered almost motionless.

The squire, however, sent after his sister the same holloa which attends the departure of a hare, when she is first started before the hounds. He was indeed a great master of this kind of vociferation, and had a holla proper for most occasions in life.

[5] German: a reference to the fact that the King and many of the court were of German extraction

A Muddy Accident

from *The Life and Opinions of Tristram Shandy*

by Laurence Sterne

Tristram Shandy recounts the circumstances of his birth. He
tells us what happened when the servant Obadiah set out to
fetch Doctor Slop, the male midwife, and accidentally ran into
him on the way.

Imagine to yourself a little squat, uncourtly figure of a
Doctor Slop, of about four feet and a half perpendicular height, with a breadth of back, and a sesquipedality
of belly,[1] which might have done honour to a serjeant in
the horse-guards.

Such were the outlines of Dr Slop's figure, which – if
you have read Hogarth's analysis of beauty, and if you
have not, I wish you would; — you must know, may as
certainly be caricatured, and conveyed to the mind by
three strokes as three hundred.

Imagine such a one, — for such, I say, were the
outlines of Dr Slop's figure, coming slowly along, foot
by foot, waddling through the dirt upon the vertebræ of
a little diminutive pony, of a pretty colour; — but of
strength, — alack! — scarce able to have made an
amble of it, under such a fardel, had the roads been in
an ambling condition. — They were not. — Imagine to
yourself, Obadiah mounted upon a strong monster of a
coach-horse, pricked into a full gallop, and making all
practicable speed the adverse way.

[1] a stomach that sticks out one and a half feet

Pray, Sir, let me interest you a moment in this description.

Had Dr Slop beheld Obadiah a mile off, posting in a narrow lane directly towards him, at that monstrous rate, – splashing and plunging like a devil through thick and thin, as he approached, would not such a phenomenon, with such a vortex of mud and water moving along with it, round its axis, – have been a subject of juster apprehension to Dr Slop in his situation, than the *worst* of Whiston's comets? – To say nothing of the NUCLEUS; that is, of Obadiah and the coach-horse. – In my idea, the vortex alone of 'em was enough to have involved and carried, if not the doctor, at least the doctor's pony, quite away with it. What then do you think must the terror and hydrophobia of Dr Slop have been, when you read (which you are just going to do) that he was advancing thus warily along towards Shandy Hall, and had approached to within sixty yards of it, and within five yards of a sudden turn, made by an acute angle of the garden-wall, – and in the dirtiest part of a dirty lane, – when Obadiah and his coach-horse turned the corner, rapid, furious, – pop, – full upon him! – Nothing, I think, in nature, can be supposed more terrible than such a Rencounter, – so imprompt! so ill prepared to stand the shock of it as Dr Slop was!

What could Dr Slop do? — He crossed himself+ – Pugh! – but the doctor, Sir, was a Papist.[2] – No matter; he had better have kept hold of the pummel. – He had so; – nay as it happened, he had better have done nothing at all; — for in crossing himself he let go his whip, — and in attempting to save his whip betwixt his knee and his saddle's skirt, as it slipped, he lost his stirrup, — in losing which, he lost his seat; — and in the

[2] insulting term for a Roman Catholic

multitude ·of all these losses (which, by the bye, shews what little advantages there is in crossing) the unfortunate doctor lost his presence of mind. So that, without waiting for Obadiah's onset, he left his pony to its destiny, tumbling off it diagonally, something in the stile and manner of a pack of wool, and without any other consequence from the fall, save that of being left (as it would have been) with the broadest part of him sunk about twelve inches deep in the mire.

Obadiah pulled off his cap twice to Dr Slop; – once as he was falling, – and then again when he saw him seated. — Ill-timed complaisance! – had not the fellow better have stopped his horse, and got off and helped him? – Sir, he did all that his situation would allow; but the MOMENTUM of the coach-horse was so great, that Obadiah could not do it all at once; he rode in a circle three times round Dr Slop, before he could fully accomplish it any how; – and at the last, when he did stop his beast, 'twas done with such an explosion of mud, that Obadiah had better been a league off. In short, never was a Dr Slop so beluted,[3] and so transsubstantiated, since that affair came into fashion.

When Dr Slop entered the back parlour, where my father and my uncle Toby were discoursing upon the nature of women, – it was hard to determine whether Dr Slop's figure, or Dr Slop's presence, occasioned more surprise to them; for as the accident happened so near the house, as not to make it worth while for Obadiah to remount him, – Obadiah had led him in as he was, *unwiped, unappointed, unannealed*, with all his stains and blotches on him. – He stood like Hamlet's ghost, motionless and speechless, for a full minute and

3 covered in mud

a half, at the parlour door (Obadiah still holding his hand) with all the majesty of mud. His hinder parts, upon which he had received his fall, totally besmeared, — and in every other part of him, blotched over in such a manner with Obadiah's explosion, that you would have sworn (without mental reservation) that every grain of it had taken effect.

Supernatural Horror

from *The Castle of Otranto*

by Horace Walpole

This story is set in about the twelfth century in the castle of
Prince Manfred of Otranto. His fifteen-year-old son, Conrad, is
about to be married to Princess Isabella.

The company was assembled in the chapel of the castle,
and every thing ready for beginning the divine office,
when Conrad himself was missing. Manfred, impatient
of the least delay, and who had not observed his son
retire, dispatched one of his attendants to summon the
young prince. The servant, who had not staid long
enough to have crossed the court to Conrad's apartment, came running back breathless, in a frantic
manner, his eyes staring, and foaming at the mouth. He
said nothing, but pointed to the court. The company
were struck with terror and amazement. The princess
Hippolita, without knowing what was the matter, but
anxious for her son, swooned away. Manfred, less
apprehensive than enraged at the procrastination of
the nuptials, and at the folly of his domestic, asked
imperiously, what was the matter? The fellow made no
answer, but continued pointing towards the court-yard;
and at last, after repeated questions put to him, cried
out, Oh, the helmet! the helmet! In the mean time
some of the company had run into the court, from
whence was heard a confused noise of shrieks, horror,
and surprise. Manfred, who began to be alarmed at not
seeing his son, went himself to get information of what

occasioned this strange confusion. Matilda remained endeavouring to assist her mother, and Isabella staid for the same purpose, and to avoid showing any impatience for the bridegroom, for whom, in truth, she had conceived little affection.

The first thing that struck Manfred's eyes was a group of his servants endeavouring to raise something that appeared to him a mountain of sable plumes. He gazed without believing his sight. What are ye doing? cried Manfred, wrathfully: Where is my son? A volley of voices replied, Oh, my lord! the prince! the prince! the helmet! the helmet! Shocked with these lamentable sounds, and dreading he knew not what, he advanced hastily – But what a sight for a father's eyes! – He beheld his child dashed to pieces, and almost buried under an enormous helmet, an hundred times more large than any casque ever made for human being, and shaded with a proportionable quantity of black feathers.

The horror of the spectacle, the ignorance of all around how this misfortune happened, and above all, the tremendous phænomenon before him, took away the prince's speech. Yet his silence lasted longer than even grief could occasion. He fixed his eyes on what he wished in vain to believe a vision; and seemed less attentive to his loss, than buried in meditation on the stupendous object that had occasioned it. He touched, he examined the fatal casque; nor could even the bleeding mangled remains of the young prince divert the eyes of Manfred from the portent before him. All who had known his partial fondness for young Conrad, were as much surprised at their prince's insensibility, as thunderstruck themselves at the miracle of the helmet. They conveyed the disfigured corse into the hall, without receiving the least direction from Manfred. As little was he attentive to the ladies who remained in the chapel: on the contrary, without mentioning the unhappy princesses his wife and daughter, the first sounds that dropped from Manfred's lips were, Take care of the lady Isabella. . . .

Following this disaster, a peasant boy identifies the helmet as like that belonging to a statue of a former prince. Manfred accuses the peasant of black magic and confines him beneath the helmet, then tells Isabella that he is going to divorce his wife and marry her himself. The horrified Isabella escapes from him into the underground passages of the castle.

The lower part of the castle was hollowed into several intricate cloisters; and it was not easy for one under so much anxiety to find the door that opened into the cavern. An awful silence reigned throughout those subterraneous regions, except now and then some blasts of wind that shook the doors she had passed, and which grating on the rusty hinges were re-echoed through that long labyrinth of darkness. Every murmur struck her with new terror; yet more she dreaded to hear the wrathful voice of Manfred urging his domestics to pursue her. She trod as softly as impatience would give her leave, yet frequently stopped and listened to hear if she was followed. In one of those moments she thought she heard a sigh. She shuddered, and recoiled a few paces. In a moment she thought she heard the step of some person. Her blood curdled; she concluded it was Manfred. Every suggestion that horror could inspire rushed into her mind. She condemned her rash flight, which had thus exposed her to his rage in a place where her cries were not likely to draw any body to her assistance. Yet the sound seemed not to come from behind; if Manfred knew where she was, he must have followed her: she was still in one of the cloisters, and the steps she had heard were too distinct to proceed from the way she had come. Cheered with this reflection, and hoping to find a friend in whoever was not the prince; she was going to advance, when a door that stood ajar, at some distance to the left, was opened gently; but ere her lamp, which she held up, could discover who opened it, the person retreated precipitately on seeing the light.

Isabella, whom every incident was sufficient to dismay, hesitated whether she should proceed. Her dread of Manfred soon outweighed every other terror. The very circumstance of the person avoiding her, gave her a sort of courage. It could only be, she thought, some domestic belonging to the castle. Her gentleness had never raised her an enemy, and conscious innocence made her hope that, unless sent by the prince's order to seek her, his servants would rather assist than prevent her flight. Fortifying herself with these reflections, and believing, by what she could observe, that she was near the mouth of the subterraneous cavern, she approached the door that had been opened; but a sudden gust of wind that met her at the door extinguished her lamp, and left her in total darkness.

Words cannot paint the horror of the princess's situation. Alone in so dismal a place, her mind imprinted with all the terrible events of the day, hopeless of escaping, expecting every moment the arrival of Manfred, and far from tranquil on knowing she was within reach of somebody, she knew not whom, who for some cause seemed concealed thereabouts, all these thoughts crowded on her distracted mind, and she was ready to sink under her apprehensions. She addressed herself to every saint in heaven, and inwardly implored their assistance. For a considerable time she remained in an agony of despair. At last, as softly as was possible, she felt for the door, and, having found it, entered trembling into the vault from whence she had heard the sigh and steps. It gave her a kind of momentary joy to perceive an imperfect ray of clouded moonshine gleam from the roof of the vault, which seemed to be fallen in, and from whence hung a fragment of earth or building, she could not distinguish which, that appeared to have been crushed inwards. She advanced eagerly towards this chasm, when she discerned a human form standing close against the wall.

She shrieked, believing it the ghost of her betrothed Conrad. The figure advancing, said in a submissive voice, Be not alarmed, lady; I will not injure you. Isabella, a little encouraged by the words and tone of voice of the stranger, and recollecting that this must be the person who had opened the door, recovered her spirits enough to reply, Sir, whoever you are, take pity on a wretched princess standing on the brink of destruction: assist me to escape from this fatal castle, or in a few moments I may be made miserable for ever. Alas! said the stranger, what can I do to assist you? I will die in your defence; but I am unacquainted with the castle, and want—Oh! said Isabella, hastily interrupting him, help me but to find a trap-door that must be hereabout, and it is the greatest service you can do me; for I have not a minute to lose. Saying these words she felt about on the pavement, and directed the stranger to search likewise for a smooth piece of brass inclosed in one of the stones. That, said she, is the lock, which opens with a spring, of which I know the secret. If I can find that, I may escape – if not, alas, courteous stranger, I fear I shall have involved you in my misfortunes: Manfred will suspect you for the accomplice of my flight, and you will fall a victim to his resentment. I value not my life, said the stranger; and it will be some comfort to lose it in trying to deliver you from his tyranny. Generous youth, said Isabella, how shall I ever requite—As she uttered those words, a ray of moonshine streaming through a cranny of the ruin above shone directly on the lock they sought – Oh, transport! said Isabella, here is the trap-door! and taking out a key, she touched the spring, which starting aside discovered an iron ring. Lift up the door, said the princess. The stranger obeyed; and beneath appeared some stone steps descending into a vault totally dark. We must go down here, said Isabella: follow me; dark and dismal as it is, we cannot miss our way; it leads directly to the church of saint Nicholas – But perhaps, added the princess modestly, you have no reason to leave the castle, nor have I farther occasion for your service; in a few minutes I shall be safe from Manfred's rage – only let me know to whom I am so much obliged. I will never quit you, said the stranger eagerly, till I have placed you in safety – nor think me, princess, more generous than I am: though you are my principal care—The stranger was interrupted by a sudden noise of voices that seemed approaching, and they soon distinguished these words: Talk not to me of necromancers;[1] I tell you she must be in the castle; I will find her in spite of enchantment. Oh, heavens! cried Isabella, it is the voice of Manfred! Make haste, or we are ruined! and shut the trap-door after you. Saying this, she descended the steps precipitately; and as the stranger hastened to follow her, he let the door slip out of his hands: it fell, and the spring closed over it. He tried in vain to open it, not having observed Isabella's method of touching the spring, nor had he many moments to make an essay.

[1] evil magicians, especially those who communicate with the dead

The noise of the falling door had been heard by Manfred, who, directed by the sound, hastened thither, attended by his servants with torches. It must be Isabella, cried Manfred before he entered the vault; she is escaping by the subterraneous passage, but she cannot have got far. What was the astonishment of the prince, when, instead of Isabella, the light of the torches discovered to him the young peasant, whom he thought confined under the fatal helmet!

An Embarrassing Encounter

from *Evelina*

by Fanny Burney

Evelina, a young girl on her first visit to London in the care of
Mrs Mirvan and her daughter, writes to her guardian, the
Reverend Mr Villars, about everything that happens to her.

Evelina to the Rev. Mr Villars

> *Queen Ann Street, London, Saturday, 2 April*

This moment arrived. Just going to Drury Lane
Theatre. The celebrated Mr Garrick[1] performs Ranger.
I am quite in extacy. So is Miss Mirvan. How fortunate,
that he should happen to play! We would not let
Mrs Mirvan rest till she consented to go; her chief
objection was to our dress, for we have had no time to
Londonise ourselves; but we teized her into compliance,
and so we are to sit in some obscure place, that she may
not be seen. As to me, I should be alike unknown in the
most conspicuous or most private part of the house.

I can write no more now. I hardly have time to
breathe – only just this, the houses and streets are not
quite so superb as I expected. However, I have seen
nothing yet, so I ought not to judge.

Well, adieu, my dearest Sir, for the present; I could
not forbear writing a few words instantly on my arrival;

[1] a celebrated actor of the day

though I suppose my letter of thanks for your consent is still on the road.

Saturday night

O my dear Sir, in what raptures am I returned! Well may Mr Garrick be so celebrated, so universally admired – I had not any idea of so great a performer.

Such ease! such vivacity in his manner! such grace in his motions! such fire and meaning in his eyes! – I could hardly believe he had studied a written part, for every word seemed to be uttered from the impulse of the moment.

His action – at once so graceful and so free! – his voice – so clear, so melodious, yet so wonderfully various in its tones – such animation! – every look *speaks*!

I would have given the world to have had the whole play acted over again. And when he danced – O how I envied Clarinda! I almost wished to have jumped on the stage and joined them.

I am afraid you will think me mad, so I won't say any more; yet I really believe Mr Garrick would make you mad too, if you could see him. I intend to ask Mrs Mirvan to go to the play every night while we stay in town. She is extremely kind to me, and Maria, her charming daughter, is the sweetest girl in the world.

I shall write to you every evening all that passes in the day, and that in the same manner as, if I could see, I should tell you. . . .

Monday

We are to go this evening to a private ball, given by Mrs Stanley, a very fashionable lady of Mrs Mirvan's acquaintance.

We have been a *shopping*, as Mrs Mirvan calls it, all this morning, to buy silks, caps, gauzes, and so forth.

The shops are really very entertaining, especially the mercers; there seem to be six or seven men belonging to each shop, and everyone took care, by bowing and smirking, to be noticed; we were conducted from one to another, and carried from room to room, with so much ceremony, that at first I was almost afraid to go on.

I thought I should never have chosen a silk, for they produced so many, I knew not which to fix upon, and they recommended them all so strongly, that I fancy they thought I only wanted persuasion to buy everything they showed me. And, indeed, they took so much trouble, that I was almost ashamed I could not.

At the milliners, the ladies we met were so much dressed, that I should rather have imagined they were making visits than purchases. But what most diverted [me] was, that we were more frequently served by men than by women; and such men! so finical, so affected! they seemed to understand every part of a woman's dress better than we do ourselves; and they recommended caps and ribbands with an air of so much importance, that I wished to ask them how long they had left off wearing them!

The dispatch with which they work in these great shops is amazing, for they have promised me a compleat suit of linen against the evening.

I have just had my hair dressed. You can't think how oddly my head feels; full of powder and black pins, and a great *cushion* on the top of it. I believe you would hardly know me, for my face looks quite different to what it did before my hair was dressed. When I shall be able to make use of a comb for myself I cannot tell, for my hair is so much entangled, *frizled* they call it, that I fear it will be very difficult.

I am half afraid of this ball tonight, for, you know, I have never danced but at school; however, Miss Mirvan says there is nothing in it. Yet I wish it was over.

Adieu, my dear Sir; pray excuse the wretched stuff I write, perhaps I may improve by being in this town, and then my letters will be less unworthy your reading. Mean time I am,

Your dutiful and affectionate, though unpolished,

EVELINA

Poor Miss Mirvan cannot wear one of the caps she made, because they dress her hair too large for them.

Evelina in continuation

Queen Ann Street, 5 April, Tuesday Morning

I have a vast deal to say, and shall give all this morning to my pen. As to my plan of writing every evening the adventures of the day, I find it impracticable; for the diversions here are so very late, that if I begin my letters after them, I could not go to bed at all.

We past a most extraordinary evening. A *private* ball this was called, so I expected to have seen about four or five couple; but Lord! my dear Sir, I believe I saw half the world! Two very large rooms were full of company; in one, were cards for the elderly ladies, and in the other, were the dancers. My mamma Mirvan, for she always calls me her child, said she would sit with Maria and me till we were provided with partners, and then join the card-players.

The gentlemen, as they passed and repassed, looked as if they thought we were quite at their disposal, and only waiting for the honour of their commands; and they sauntered about, in a careless indolent manner, as if with a view to keep us in suspense. I don't speak of this in regard to Miss Mirvan and myself only, but to the ladies in general; and I thought it so provoking, that I determined, in my own mind, that, far from humouring such airs, I would rather not dance at all, than with anyone who should seem to think me ready to accept the first partner who would condescend to take me.

Not long after, a young man, who had for some time looked at us with a kind of negligent impertinence, advanced, on tip-toe, towards me; he had a set smile on his face, and his dress was so foppish, that I really believe he even wished to be stared at; and yet he was very ugly.

Bowing almost to the ground, with a sort of swing, and waving his hand with the greatest conceit, after a short and silly pause, he said, 'Madam – may I presume?' and stopt, offering to take my hand. I drew it back, but could scarce forbear laughing. 'Allow me, Madam,' (continued he, affectedly breaking off every half moment) 'the honour and happiness – if I am not so unhappy as to address you too late – to have the happiness and honour –'.

Again he would have taken my hand, but, bowing my head, I begged to be excused, and turned to Miss Mirvan to conceal my laughter. He then desired to know if I had already engaged myself to some more fortunate man? I said No, and that I believed I should not dance at all. He would keep himself, he told me, disengaged, in hopes I should relent; and then, uttering some ridiculous speeches of sorrow and disappointment, though his face still wore the same invariable smile, he retreated.

It so happened, as we have since recollected, that

during this little dialogue, Mrs Mirvan was conversing with the lady of the house. And very soon after another gentleman, who seemed about six-and-twenty years old, gayly, but not foppishly, dressed, and indeed extremely handsome, with an air of mixed politeness and gallantry, desired to know if I was engaged, or would honour him with my hand. So he was pleased to say, though I am sure I know not what honour he could receive from me; but these sort of expressions, I find, are used as words of course, without any distinction of persons, or study of propriety.

Well, I bowed, and I am sure I coloured; for indeed I was frightened at the thoughts of dancing before so many people, all strangers, and, which was worse, *with* a stranger; however, that was unavoidable, for though I looked round the room several times, I could not see one person that I knew. And so, he took my hand, and led me to join in the dance.

The minuets were over before we arrived, for we were kept late by the milliners making us wait for our things.

He seemed very desirous of entering into conversation with me; but I was seized with such a panic, that I could hardly speak a word, and nothing but the shame of so soon changing my mind, prevented my returning to my seat, and declining to dance at all.

He appeared to be surprised at my terror, which I believe was but too apparent: however, he asked no questions, though I fear he must think it very strange; for I did not choose to tell him it was owing to my never before dancing but with a school-girl.

His conversation was sensible and spirited; his air and address were open and noble; his manners gentle, attentive, and infinitely engaging; his person is all elegance, and his countenance, the most animated and expressive I have ever seen.

In a short time we were joined by Miss Mirvan, who stood next couple to us. But how was I startled, when she whispered me that my partner was a nobleman! This gave me a new alarm; how will he be provoked, thought I, when he finds what a simple rustic he has honoured with his choice! one whose ignorance of the world makes her perpetually fear doing something wrong!

That he should be so much my superior every way, quite disconcerted me; and you will suppose my spirits were not much raised, when I heard a lady, in passing us, say, 'This is the most difficult dance I ever saw.'

'O dear, then,' cried Maria to her partner, 'with your leave, I'll sit down till the next.'

'So will I too, then,' cried I, 'for I am sure I can hardly stand.'

'But you must speak to your partner first,' answered she; for he had turned aside to talk with some gentlemen. However, I had not sufficient courage to address him, and so away we all three tript, and seated ourselves at another end of the room.

But, unfortunately for me, Miss Mirvan soon after suffered herself to be prevailed upon to attempt the dance; and just as she rose to go, she cried, 'My dear, yonder is your partner, Lord Orville, walking about the room in search of you.'

'Don't leave me then, dear girl!' cried I; but she was obliged to go. And now I was more uneasy then ever; I would have given the world to have seen Mrs Mirvan, and begged of her to make my apologies; for what, thought I, can I possibly say to him in excuse for running away? he must either conclude me a fool, or half mad; for anyone brought up in the great world, and accustomed to its ways, can have no idea of such sort of fears as mine.

My confusion increased when I observed that he was everywhere seeking me, with apparent perplexity and surprise; but when, at last, I saw him move towards the place where I sat, I was ready to sink with shame and distress. I found it absolutely impossible to keep my seat, because I could not think of a word to say for myself, and so I rose, and walked hastily towards the card-room, resolving to stay with Mrs Mirvan the rest of the evening, and not to dance at all. But before I could find her, Lord Orville saw and approached me.

He begged to know if I was not well? You may easily imagine how much I was embarrassed. I made no answer, but hung my head, like a fool, and looked on my fan.

He then, with an air the most respectfully serious, asked if he had been so unhappy as to offend me?

'No indeed!' cried I: and, in hopes of changing the discourse, and preventing his further inquiries, I desired to know if he had seen the young lady who had been conversing with me?

No;—but would I honour him with any commands to her?

'O, by no means!'

Was there any other person with whom I wished to speak?

I said *no*, before I knew I had answered at all.

Should he have the pleasure of bringing me any refreshment?

I bowed, almost involuntarily. And away he flew.

I was quite ashamed of being so troublesome, and so much *above* myself as these seeming airs made me appear; but indeed I was too much confused to think or act with any consistency.

If he had not been swift as lightning, I don't know whether I should not have stolen away again; but he returned in a moment. When I had drunk a glass of lemonade, he hoped, he said, that I would again honour him with my hand as a new dance was just begun. I had not the presence of mind to say a single word, and so I let him once more lead me to the place I had left. . . .

They dance together, then sit down again.

We were sitting in this manner, he conversing with all gaiety, I looking down with all foolishness, when that fop who had first asked me to dance, with a most ridiculous solemnity, approached, and after a profound bow or two, said, 'I humbly beg pardon, Madam, – and of you too, my Lord, – for breaking in upon such agreeable conversation – which must, doubtless, be much more delectable – than what I have the honour to offer – but – '

I interrupted him – I blush for my folly, – with laughing; yet I could not help it, for, added to the man's stately foppishness (and he actually took snuff between every three words), when I looked round at Lord Orville, I saw such extreme surprise in his face, – the cause of which appeared so absurd, that I could not for my life preserve my gravity.

I had not laughed before from the time I had left Miss Mirvan, and I had much better have cried then; Lord Orville actually stared at me; the beau, I know not his name, looked quite enraged. 'Refrain – Madam,' (said he, with an important air), 'a few moments refrain! – I have but a sentence to trouble you with. – May I know to what accident I must attribute not having the honour of your hand?'

'Accident, Sir!' repeated I, much astonished.

'Yes, accident, Madam – for surely – I must take the

liberty to observe – pardon me, Madam – it ought to be no common one – that should tempt a lady – so young a one, too – to be guilty of ill-manners.'

A confused idea now for the first time entered my head, of something I had heard of the rules of an assembly; but I was never at one before, – I have only danced at school, – and so giddy and heedless I was, that I had not once considered the impropriety of refusing one partner, and afterwards accepting another. I was thunderstruck at the recollection: but while these thoughts were rushing into my head, Lord Orville, with some warmth, said, 'This lady, Sir, is incapable of meriting such an accusation!'

The creature – for I am very angry with him – made a low bow, and with a grip the most malicious I ever saw, 'My Lord,' said he, 'far be it from me to *accuse* the lady, for having the discernment to distinguish and prefer – the superior attractions of your Lordship.'

Again he bowed, and walked off.

Was ever anything so provoking? I was ready to die with shame. 'What a coxcomb!' exclaimed Lord Orville; while I, without knowing what I did, rose hastily, and moving off, 'I can't imagine,' cried I, 'where Mrs Mirvan has hid herself!'

'Give me leave to see,' answered he. I bowed and sat down again, not daring to meet his eyes; for what must he think of me, between my blunder, and the supposed preference?

He returned in a moment, and told me that Mrs Mirvan was at cards, but would be glad to see me; and I went immediately. There was but one chair vacant, so, to my great relief, Lord Orville presently left us. I then told Mrs Mirvan my disasters, and she good-naturedly blamed herself for not having better instructed me, but said she had taken it for granted that

I must know such common customs. However, the man may, I think, be satisfied with his pretty speech, and carry his resentment no farther.

In a short time, Lord Orville returned. I consented, with the best grace I could, to go down another dance, for I had had time to recollect myself, and therefore resolved to use some exertion, and, if possible, appear less a fool than I had hitherto done; for it occurred to me that, insignificant as I was, compared to a man of his rank and figure, yet since he had been so unfortunate as to make choice of me for a partner, why I should endeavour to make the best of it.

The dance, however, was short, and he spoke very little; so I had no opportunity of putting my resolution in practice. He was satisfied, I suppose, with his former successless efforts to draw me out; or, rather, I fancied, he had been inquiring *who I was*. This again disconcerted me, and the spirits I had determined to exert, again failed me. Tired, ashamed and mortified, I begged to sit down till we returned home, which I did soon after. Lord Orville did me the honour to hand me to the coach, talking all the way of the honour *I* had done *him*! O these fashionable people!

Well, my dear Sir, was it not a strange evening? I could not help being thus particular, because, to me, everything is so new. But it is now time to conclude.

I am, with all love and duty, your

EVELINA

Alarming Young Men

from *Northanger Abbey*

by Jane Austen

Catherine Morland has recently arrived in the popular resort of Bath. This is her first taste of fashionable society and she is easily impressed by her sophisticated new friend, Isabella Thorpe. They discover that they share a taste for Gothic or sensationalist novels. In this extract, they visit the Pump-room (a room for drinking spa-water and socialising), where they divide their time between discussing their favourite novels and watching the young men.

The following conversation, which took place between the two friends in the Pump-room one morning, after an acquaintance of eight or nine days, is given as a specimen of their very warm attachment, and of the delicacy, discretion, originality of thought, and literary taste which marked the reasonableness of that attachment.

They met by appointment; and as Isabella had arrived nearly five minutes before her friend, her first address naturally was – 'My dearest creature, what can have made you so late? I have been waiting for you at least this age!'

'Have you, indeed! – I am very sorry for it; but really I thought I was in very good time. It is but just one. I hope you have not been here long?'

'Oh! these ten ages at least. I am sure I have been here this half hour. But now, let us go and sit down at the other end of the room, and enjoy ourselves. I have an hundred things to say to you. In the first place, I was so afraid it would rain this morning, just as I wanted to set off; it looked very showery, and that would have thrown me into agonies! Do you know, I saw the prettiest hat you can imagine, in a shop window in Milsom-street just now – very like yours, only with coquelicot[1] ribbons instead of green; I quite longed for it. But, my dearest Catherine, what have you been doing with yourself all this morning? – Have you gone on with Udolpho?'

'Yes, I have been reading it ever since I woke; and I am got to the black veil.'

'Are you, indeed? How delightful! Oh! I would not tell you what is behind the black veil for the world! Are not you wild to know?'

'Oh! yes, quite; what can it be? – But do not tell me – I would not be told upon any account. I know it must be a skeleton, I am sure it is Laurentina's skeleton. Oh! I am delighted with the book! I should like to spend my whole life in reading it. I assure you, if it had not been to meet you, I would not have come away from it for all the world.'

'Dear creature! how much I am obliged to you; and when you have finished Udolpho, we will read the Italian together; and I have made out a list of ten or twelve more of the same kind for you.'

'Have you, indeed! How glad I am! – What are they all?'

'I will read you their names directly; here they are, in my pocket-book. Castle of Wolfenbach, Clermont, Mysterious Warnings, Necromancer of the Black Forest, Midnight Bell, Orphan of the Rhine, and Horrid Mysteries. Those will last us some time.'

[1] reddish-orange

'Yes, pretty well; but are they all horrid, are you sure they are all horrid?'

'Yes, quite sure; for a particular friend of mine, a Miss Andrews, a sweet girl, one of the sweetest creatures in the world, has read every one of them. I wish you knew Miss Andrews, you would be delighted with her. She is netting herself the sweetest cloak you can conceive. I think her as beautiful as an angel, and I am so vexed with the men for not admiring her! – I scold them all amazingly about it.'

'Scold them! Do you scold them for not admiring her?'

'Yes, that I do. There is nothing I would not do for those who are really my friends. I have no notion of loving people by halves, it is not my nature. My attachments are always excessively strong. I told Capt. Hunt at one of our assemblies this winter, that if he was to tease me all night, I would not dance with him, unless he would allow Miss Andrews to be as beautiful as an angel. The men think us incapable of real friendship you know, and I am determined to shew them the difference. Now, if I were to hear any body speak slightingly of you, I should fire up in a moment: – but that is not at all likely, for you are just the kind of girl to be a great favourite with the men.'

'Oh! dear,' cried Catherine, colouring, 'how can you say so?'

'I know you very well; you have so much animation, which is exactly what Miss Andrews wants, for I must confess there is something amazingly insipid about her. Oh! I must tell you, that just after we parted yesterday, I saw a young man looking at you so earnestly – I am sure he is in love with you.' Catherine coloured, and disclaimed again. Isabella laughed. 'It is very true, upon my honour, but I see how it is; you are indifferent to every body's admiration, except that of one gentleman, who shall be nameless. Nay, I cannot blame you – (speaking more seriously) – your feelings are easily understood. Where the heart is really attached, I know very well how little one can be pleased with the attention of any body else. Every thing is so insipid, so uninteresting, that does not relate to the beloved object! I can perfectly comprehend your feelings.'

'But you should not persuade me that I think so very much about Mr Tilney, for perhaps I may never see him again.'

'Not see him again! My dearest creature, do not talk of it. I am sure you would be miserable if you thought so.'

'No, indeed, I should not. I do not pretend to say that I was not very much pleased with him; but while I have Udolpho to read, I feel as if nobody could make me miserable. Oh! the dreadful black veil! My dear Isabella, I am sure there must be Laurentina's skeleton behind it.'

'It is so odd to me, that you should never have read Udolpho before; but I suppose Mrs Morland objects to novels.'

'No, she does not. She very often reads Sir Charles Grandison herself; but new books do not fall in our way.'

'Sir Charles Grandison! That is an amazing horrid book, is it not? – I remember Miss Andrews could not get through the first volume.'

'It is not like Udolpho at all; but yet I think it is very entertaining.'

'Do you indeed! – you surprize me; I thought it had not been readable. But, my dearest Catherine, have you settled what to wear on your head to-night? I am determined at all events to be dressed exactly like you. The men take notice of that sometimes you know.'

'But it does not signify if they do;' said Catherine, very innocently.

'Signify! Oh, heavens! I make it a rule never to mind what they say. They are very often amazingly impertinent if you do not treat them with spirit, and make them keep their distance.'

'Are they? – Well, I never observed that. They always behave very well to me.'

'Oh! they give themselves such airs. They are the most conceited creatures in the world, and think themselves of so much importance! – By the bye, though I have thought of it a hundred times, I have always forgot to ask you what is your favourite complexion in a man. Do you like them best dark or fair?'

'I hardly know. I never much thought about it. Something between both, I think. Brown – not fair, and not very dark.'

'Very well, Catherine. That is exactly he. I have not forgot your description of Mr Tilney; – "a brown skin, with dark eyes, and rather dark hair." – Well, my taste is different. I prefer light eyes, and as to complexion – do you know – I like a sallow better than any other. You must not betray me, if you should ever meet with one of your acquaintance answering that description.'

'Betray you! – What do you mean?'

'Nay, do not distress me. I believe I have said too much. Let us drop the subject.'

Catherine, in some amazement, complied; and after remaining a few moments silent, was on the point of reverting to what interested her at that time rather more than any thing else in the world, Laurentina's skeleton; when her friend prevented her, by saying, – 'For Heaven's sake! let us move away from this end of the room. Do you know, there are two odious young men who have been staring at me this half hour.

They really put me quite out of countenance. Let us go and look at the arrivals. They will hardly follow us there.'

Away they walked to the book; and while Isabella examined the names, it was Catherine's employment to watch the proceedings of these alarming young men.

'They are not coming this way, are they? I hope they are not so impertinent as to follow us. Pray let me know if they are coming. I am determined I will not look up.'

In a few moments Catherine, with unaffected pleasure, assured her that she need not be longer uneasy, as the gentlemen had just left the Pump-room.

'And which way are they gone?' said Isabella, turning hastily round. 'One was a very good-looking young man.'

'They went towards the churchyard.'

'Well, I am amazingly glad I have got rid of them! And now, what say you to going to Edgar's Buildings with me, and looking at my new hat? You said you should like to see it.'

Catherine readily agreed. 'Only,' she added, 'perhaps we may overtake the two young men.'

'Oh! never mind that. If we make haste, we shall pass by them presently, and I am dying to shew you my hat.'

'But if we only wait a few minutes, there will be no danger of our seeing them at all.'

'I shall not pay them any such compliment, I assure you. I have no notion of treating men with such respect. That is the way to spoil them.'

Catherine had nothing to oppose against such reasoning; and therefore, to shew the independence of Miss Thorpe, and her resolution of humbling the sex, they set off immediately as fast as they could walk, in pursuit of the two young men.

A Wicked Boy

from *Wuthering Heights*

by Emily Brontë

Nelly Dean, housekeeper at Wuthering Heights, remembers the wild behaviour of young Cathy Earnshaw and Heathcliff. Heathcliff was an orphan rescued by Cathy's father who has since died. Cathy's brother Hindley, the new master of Wuthering Heights, bullies the boy. One night the two children disappear.

We searched the house, above and below, and the yard, and stables; they were invisible; and, at last, Hindley in a passion told us to bolt the doors, and swore nobody should let them in that night.

The household went to bed; and I, too anxious to lie down, opened my lattice and put my head out to harken, though it rained, determined to admit them in spite of the prohibition, should they return.

In a while, I distinguished steps coming up the road, and the light of a lantern glimmering through the gate.

I threw a shawl over my head and ran to prevent them from waking Mr Earnshaw by knocking. There was Heathcliff, by himself; it gave me a start to see him alone.

'Where is Miss Catherine?' I cried hurriedly. 'No accident, I hope?'

'At Thrushcross Grange,' he answered, 'and I would have been there too, but they had not the manners to ask me to stay.'

'Well, you will catch it!' I said, 'you'll never be

content till you're sent about your business. What in the world led you wandering to Thrushcross Grange?'

'Let me get off my wet clothes, and I'll tell you all about it, Nelly,' he replied.

I bid him beware of rousing the master, and while he undressed, and I waited to put out the candle, he continued –

'Cathy and I escaped from the wash-house to have a ramble at liberty, and getting a glimpse of the Grange lights, we thought we would just go and see whether the Lintons passed their Sunday evenings standing shivering in corners, while their father and mother sat eating and drinking, and singing and laughing, and burning their eyes out before the fire. Do you think they do? Or reading sermons, and being catechised[1] by their man-servant, and set to learn a column of Scripture names, if they don't answer properly?'

'Probably not,' I responded. 'They are good children, no doubt, and don't deserve the treatment you receive, for your bad conduct.'

'Don't you cant,[2] Nelly,' he said: 'Nonsense! We ran from the top of the Heights to the park, without stopping – Catherine completely beaten in the race, because she was barefoot. You'll have to seek for her shoes in the bog tomorrow. We crept through a broken hedge, groped our way up the path, and planted ourselves on a flower-pot under the drawing-room window. The light came from thence; they had not put up the shutters, and the curtains were only half closed. Both of us were able to look in by standing on the basement, and clinging to the ledge, and we saw – ah! it was beautiful – a splendid place carpeted with crimson,

---

[1] questioned on religious knowledge
[2] preach

and crimson-covered chairs and tables, and a pure white ceiling bordered by gold, a shower of glass-drops hanging in silver chains from the centre, and shimmering with little soft tapers. Old Mr and Mrs Linton were not there. Edgar and his sister had it entirely to themselves; shouldn't they have been happy? We should have thought ourselves in heaven! And now, guess what your good children were doing? Isabella – I believe she is eleven, a year younger than Cathy – lay screaming at the' farther end of the room, shrieking as if witches were running red-hot needles into her. Edgar stood on the hearth weeping silently, and in the middle of the table sat a little dog shaking its paw and yelping, which, from their mutual accusations, we understood they had nearly pulled in two between them. The idiots! That was their pleasure! to quarrel who should hold a heap of warm hair, and each begin to cry because both, after struggling to get it, refused to take it. We laughed outright at the petted things, we did despise them! When would you catch me wishing to have what Catherine wanted? or find us by ourselves, seeking entertainment in yelling, and sobbing, and rolling on the ground, divided by the whole room? I'd not exchange, for a thousand lives, my condition here, for Edgar Linton's at Thrushcross Grange – not if I might have the privilege of flinging Joseph off the highest gable, and painting the housefront with Hindley's blood!'

'Hush, hush!' I interrupted. 'Still you have not told me, Heathcliff, how Catherine is left behind?'

'I told you we laughed,' he answered. 'The Lintons heard us, and with one accord, they shot like arrows to the door; there was silence, and then a cry, "Oh, mamma, mamma! Oh, papa! Oh, mamma, come here. Oh, papa, oh!" They really did howl out, something in that way. We made frightful noises to terrify them still more, and then we dropped off the ledge, because somebody was drawing the bars, and we felt we had better flee. I had Cathy by the hand, and was urging her on, when all at once she fell down.

' "Run, Heathcliff, run!" she whispered. "They have let the bull dog loose, and he holds me!"

'The devil had seized her ankle, Nelly; I heard his abominable snorting. She did not yell out – no! She would have scorned to do it, if she had been spitted on the horns of a mad cow. I did, though, I vociferated curses enough to annihilate any fiend in Christendom, and I got a stone and thrust it between his jaws, and tried with all my might to cram it down his throat. A beast of a servant came up with a lantern, at last, shouting –

' "Keep fast, Skulker, keep fast!"

'He changed his note, however, when he saw Skulker's game. The dog was throttled off, his huge, purple tongue hanging half a foot out of his mouth, and his pendant lips streaming with bloody slaver.

'The man took Cathy up; she was sick; not from fear, I'm certain, but from pain. He carried her in; I followed, grumbling execrations and vengeance.

' "What prey, Robert?" hallooed Linton from the entrance.

' "Skulker has caught a little girl, sir," he replied; "and there's a lad here," he added, making a clutch at me, "who looks on out-and-outer! Very like, the robbers were for putting them through the window, to open the doors to the gang after all were asleep, that they might murder us at their ease. Hold your tongue, you foul-mouthed thief, you! you shall go to the gallows for this. Mr Linton, sir, don't lay by your gun."

' "No, no, Robert," said the old fool. "The rascals

knew that yesterday was my rent-day; they thought to have me cleverly. Come in; I'll furnish them a reception. There, John, fasten the chain. Give Skulker some water, Jenny. To beard a magistrate in his stronghold, and on the Sabbath, too! where will their insolence stop? Oh, my dear Mary, look here! Don't be afraid, it is but a boy – yet, the villain scowls so plainly in his face, would it not be a kindness to the country to hang him at once, before he shows his nature in acts, as well as features?"

'He pulled me under the chandelier, and Mrs Linton placed her spectacles on her nose and raised her hands in horror. The cowardly children crept nearer also, Isabella lisping –

' "Frightful thing! Put him in the cellar, papa. He's exactly like the son of the fortune-teller, that stole my tame pheasant. Isn't he, Edgar?"

'While they examined me, Cathy came round; she heard the last speech, and laughed. Edgar Linton, after an inquisitive stare, collected sufficient wit to recognise her. They see us at church, you know, though we seldom meet them elsewhere.

' "That's Miss Earnshaw!" he whispered to his mother, "and look how Skulker has bitten her – how her foot bleeds!"

' "Miss Earnshaw? Nonsense!" cried the dame. "Miss Earnshaw scouring the country with a gipsy! And yet, my dear, the child is in mourning – surely it is – and she may be lamed for life!"

' "What culpable carelessness in her brother!" exclaimed Mr Linton, turning from me to Catherine. "I've understood from Shielders" ' (that was the curate, sir) ' "that he lets her grow up in absolute heathenism. But who is this? Where did she pick up this companion? Oho! I declare he is that strange acquisition my late neighbour made, in his journey to Liverpool – a little Lascar, or an American or Spanish castaway."

' "A wicked boy, at all events," remarked the old lady, "and quite unfit for a decent house! Did you notice his language, Linton? I'm shocked that my children should have heard it."

'I recommenced cursing – don't be angry, Nelly – and so Robert was ordered to take me off – I refused to go without Cathy – he dragged me into the garden, pushed the lantern into my hand, assured me that Mr Earnshaw should be informed of my behaviour, and bidding me march, directly, secured the door again.

'The curtains were still looped up at one corner; and I resumed my station as spy, because, if Catherine had wished to return, I intended shattering their great glass panes to a million of fragments, unless they let her out.

'She sat on the sofa quietly. Mrs Linton took off the grey cloak of the dairy maid which we had borrowed for our excursion, shaking her head, and expostulating with her, I suppose; she was a young lady and they made a distinction between her treatment and mine. Then the woman servant brought a basin of warm water, and washed her feet; and Mr Linton mixed a tumbler of negus,[3] and Isabella emptied a plate of cakes into her lap, and Edgar stood gaping at a distance. Afterwards, they dried and combed her beautiful hair, and gave her a pair of enormous slippers, and wheeled her to the fire, and I left her, as merry as she could be, dividing her food between the little dog and Skulker, whose nose she pinched as she ate; and kindling a spark of spirit in the vacant blue eyes of the Lintons – a dim reflection from her own enchanting face – I saw they were full of stupid admiration; she is so immeasurably

[3] hot sweetened wine

superior to them – to everybody on earth; is she not, Nelly?'

'There will more come of this business than you reckon on,' I answered, covering him up and extinguishing the light, 'You are incurable Heathcliff, and Mr Hindley will have to proceed to extremities, see if he won't.'

My words came truer than I desired. The luckless adventure made Earnshaw furious – And then, Mr Linton, to mend matters, paid us a visit himself, on the morrow; and read the young master such a lecture on the road he guided his family, that he was stirred to look about him, in earnest.

Heathcliff received no flogging, but he was told that the first word he spoke to Miss Catherine should ensure a dismissal; and Mrs Earnshaw undertook to keep her sister-in-law in due restraint, when she returned home; employing art, not force – with force she would have found it impossible.

Cathy stayed at Thrushcross Grange five weeks, till Christmas. By that time her ankle was thoroughly cured, and her manners much improved. The mistress visited her often, in the interval, and commenced her plan of reform by trying to raise her self-respect with fine clothes and flattery, which she took readily: so that, instead of a wild, hatless little savage jumping into the house, and rushing to squeeze us all breathless, there lighted from a handsome black pony a very dignified person, with brown ringlets falling from the cover of a feathered beaver, and a long cloth habit which she was obliged to hold up with both hands that she might sail in.

Hindley lifted her from her horse, exclaiming delightedly,

'Why, Cathy, you are quite a beauty! I should scarcely have known you – you look like a lady now – Isabella Linton is not to be compared with her, is she, Frances?'

'Isabella has not her natural advantages,' replied his wife, 'but she must mind and not grow wild again here. Ellen, help Miss Catherine off with her things – Stay, dear, you will disarrange your curls – let me untie your hat.'

I removed the habit, and there shone forth, beneath a grand plaid silk frock, white trousers, and burnished shoes; and, while her eyes sparkled joyfully when the dogs came bounding up to welcome her, she dare hardly touch them lest they should fawn upon her splendid garments.

She kissed me gently, I was all flour making the Christmas cake, and it would not have done to give me a hug; and, then, she looked round for Heathcliff. Mr and Mrs Earnshaw watched anxiously their meeting, thinking it would enable them to judge, in some measure, what grounds they had for hoping to succeed in separating the two friends.

Heathcliff was hard to discover, at first – If he were careless, and uncared for, before Catherine's absence, he had been ten times more so, since.

Nobody but I even did him the kindness to call him a dirty boy, and bid him wash himself, once a week; and children of his age, seldom have a natural pleasure in soap and water. Therefore, not to mention his clothes, which had seen three months' service, in mire and dust, and his thick uncombed hair, the surface of his face and hands was dismally beclouded. He might well skulk behind the settle, on beholding such a bright, graceful damsel enter the house, instead of a rough-headed counterpart to himself, as he expected.

'Is Heathcliff not here?' she demanded, pulling off

her gloves, and displaying fingers wonderfully whitened with doing nothing, and staying indoors.

'Heathcliff, you may come forward,' cried Mr Hindley, enjoying his discomfiture and gratified to see what a forbidding young blackguard he would be compelled to present himself. 'You may come and wish Miss Catherine welcome, like the other servants.'

Cathy, catching a glimpse of her friend in his concealment, flew to embrace him, she bestowed seven or eight kisses on his cheek within the second, and then stopped, and drawing back, burst into a laugh, exclaiming,

'Why, how very black and cross you look! and how – how funny and grim! But that's because I'm used to Edgar, and Isabella Linton, Well, Heathcliff, have you forgotten me?'

She had some reason to put the question, for shame, and pride threw double gloom over his countenance, and kept him immovable.

'Shake hands, Heathcliff,' said Mr Earnshaw, condescendingly; 'once in a way, that is permitted.'

'I shall not!' replied the boy, finding his tongue at last. 'I shall not stand to be laughed at, I shall not bear it!'

And he would have broken from the circle, but Miss Cathy seized him again.

'I did not mean to laugh at you,' she said, 'I could not hinder myself. Heathcliff, shake hands, at least! What are you sulky for? It was only that you looked odd – If you wash your face, and brush your hair it will be all right. But you are so dirty!'

She gazed concernedly at the dusky fingers she held in her own, and also at her dress, which she feared had gained no embellishment from its contact with his.

'You needn't have touched me!' he answered, following her eye and snatching away his hand. 'I shall be as dirty as I please, and I like to be dirty, and I will be dirty.'

With that he dashed head foremost out of the room, amid the merriment of the master and mistress; and to the serious disturbance of Catherine, who could not comprehend how her remarks should have produced such an exhibition of bad temper. . . .

Nelly helps Heathcliff to clean himself up. She comforts him by telling him that he is handsome and might be a prince in disguise.

So I chattered on; and Heathcliff gradually lost his frown, and began to look quite pleasant; when all at once our conversation was interrupted by a rumbling sound moving up the road and entering the court. He ran to the window, and I to the door, just in time to behold the two Lintons descend from the family carriage, smothered in cloaks and furs, and the Earnshaws dismount from their horses – they often rode to church in winter. Catherine took a hand of each of the children, and brought them into the house, and set them before the fire, which quickly put colour into their white faces.

I urged my companion to hasten now, and show his amiable humour, and he willingly obeyed: but ill-luck would have it that, as he opened the door leading from the kitchen on one side, Hindley opened it on the other; they met, and the master, irritated at seeing him clean and cheerful, or, perhaps, eager to keep his promise to Mrs Linton, shoved him back with a sudden thrust, and angrily bade Joseph 'keep the fellow out of the room – send him into the garret till dinner is over.

He'll be cramming his fingers in the tarts, and stealing the fruit, if left alone with them a minute.'

'Nay, sir,' I could not avoid answering, 'he'll touch nothing, not he – and, I suppose, he must have his share of the dainties as well as we.'

'He shall have his share of my hand, if I catch him down stairs again till dark,' cried Hindley. 'Begone, you vagabond! What, you are attempting the coxcomb, are you? Wait till I get hold of those elegant locks – see if I won't pull them a bit longer!'

'They are long enough already,' observed Master Linton, peeping from the doorway; 'I wonder they don't make his head ache. It's like a colt's mane over his eyes!'

He ventured this remark without any intention to insult; but Heathcliff's violent nature was not prepared to endure the appearance of impertinence from one whom he seemed to hate, even then, as a rival. He seized a tureen of hot apple sauce, the first thing that came under his gripe, and dashed it full against the speaker's face and neck – who instantly commenced a lament that brought Isabella and Catherine hurrying to the place.

Mr Earnshaw snatched up the culprit directly and conveyed him to his chamber, where, doubtless, he administered a rough remedy to cool the fit of passion, for he re-appeared red and breathless. I got the dish-cloth, and, rather spitefully, scrubbed Edgar's nose and mouth, affirming it served him right for meddling. His sister began weeping to go home, and Cathy stood by confounded, blushing for all.

'You should not have spoken to him!' she expostulated with Master Linton. 'He was in a bad temper, and now you've spoilt your visit, and he'll be flogged – I hate him to be flogged! I can't eat my dinner. Why did you speak to him, Edgar?'

'I didn't,' sobbed the youth, escaping from my hands, and finishing the remainder of the purification with his cambric pocket-handkerchief. 'I promised mamma that I wouldn't say one word to him, and I didn't.'

'Well, don't cry!' replied Catherine, contemptuously. 'You're not killed – don't make more mischief – my brother is coming – be quiet! Give over, Isabella! Has anybody hurt *you?*'

'There, there, children – to your seats!' cried Hindley, bustling in. 'That brute of a lad has warmed me nicely. Next time, Master Edgar, take the law into your own fists – it will give you an appetite!'

The little party recovered its equanimity at sight of the fragrant feast. They were hungry after their ride, and easily consoled, since no real harm had befallen them.

Mr Earnshaw carved bountiful platefuls; and the mistress made them merry with lively talk. I waited behind her chair, and was pained to behold Catherine, with dry eyes and an indifferent air, commence cutting up the wing of a goose before her.

'An unfeeling child,' I thought to myself, 'how lightly she dismisses her old playmate's troubles. I could not have imagined her to be so selfish.'

She lifted a mouthful to her lips; then, set it down again: her cheeks flushed, and the tears gushed over them. She slipped her fork to the floor, and hastily dived under the cloth to conceal her emotion. I did not call her unfeeling long, for, I perceived, she was in purgatory throughout the day, and wearying to find an opportunity of getting by herself, or paying a visit to Heathcliff, who had been locked up by the master, as I discovered, on endeavouring to introduce to him a private mess of victuals.

In the evening we had a dance. Cathy begged that he

might be liberated then, as Isabella Linton had no partner; her entreaties were vain, and I was appointed to supply the deficiency.

We got rid of all gloom in the excitement of the exercise, and our pleasure was increased by the arrival of the Gimmerton band, mustering fifteen strong; a trumpet, a trombone, clarionets, bassoons, French horns, and a bass viol, besides singers. They go the rounds of all the respectable houses, and receive contributions every Christmas, and we esteemed it a first-rate treat to hear them.

After the usual carols had been sung, we set them to songs and glees. Mrs Earnshaw loved the music, and, so, they gave us plenty.

Catherine loved it too; but she said it sounded sweetest at the top of the steps, and she went up in the dark; I followed. They shut the house door below, never noting our absence, it was so full of people. She made no stay at the stairs' head, but mounted farther, to the garret where Heathcliff was confined; and called him. He stubbornly declined answering for a while - she persevered, and finally persuaded him to hold communion with her through the boards.

I let the poor things converse unmolested, till I supposed the songs were going to cease, and the singers to get some refreshment: then, I clambered up the ladder to warn her.

Instead of finding her outside, I heard her voice within. The little monkey had crept by the skylight of one garret, along the roof, into the skylight of the other, and it was with the utmost difficulty I could coax her out again.

When she did come, Heathcliff came with her; and she insisted that I should take him into the kitchen, as my fellow-servant had gone to a neighbour's to be removed from the sound of our 'devil's psalmody,' as it pleased him to call it. I told them I intended, by no means, to encourage their tricks; but as the prisoner had never broken his fast since yesterday's dinner, I would wink at his cheating Mr Hindley that once.

He went down; I set him a stool by the fire, and offered him a quantity of good things; but, he was sick and could eat little: and my attempts to entertain him were thrown away. He leant his two elbows on his knees, and his chin on his hands, and remained wrapt in dumb meditation.

On my inquiring the subject of his thoughts, he answered gravely –

'I'm trying to settle how I shall pay Hindley back. I don't care how long I wait, if I can only do it, at last. I hope he will not die before I do!'

'For shame, Heathcliff!' said I. 'It is for God to punish wicked people; we should learn to forgive.'

'No, God won't have the satisfaction that I shall,' he returned. 'I only wish I knew the best way! Let me alone, and I'll plan it out: while I'm thinking of that, I don't feel pain.'

Bully!

from *Vanity Fair*

by William Thackeray

This extract takes us back to the schooldays of William Dobbin
and George Osborne at Dr Swishtail's boarding school for
boys. Dobbin, or 'Figs' as he is nicknamed, is teased by the
other boys because his father is a grocer. Cuff is another boy at
the school.

Cuff's fight with Dobbin, and the unexpected issue of
that contest, will long be remembered by every man
who was educated at Dr Swishtail's famous school. The
latter youth (who used to be called Heigh-ho Dobbin,
Gee-ho Dobbin, and by many other names indicative of
puerile[1] contempt) was the quietest, the clumsiest, and,
as it seemed, the dullest of all Dr Swishtail's young
gentlemen. His parent was a grocer in the City: and
it was bruited abroad that he was admitted into
Dr Swishtail's academy upon what are called 'mutual
principles' – that is to say, the expenses of his board and
schooling were defrayed by his father in goods, not
money; and he stood there – almost at the bottom of
the school – in his scraggy corduroys and jacket,
through the seams of which his great big bones were
bursting – as the representative of so many pounds of
tea, candles, sugar, mottled-soap, plums (of which a
very mild proportion was supplied for the puddings of
the establishment), and other commodities. A dreadful

[1] childish, schoolboyish

day it was for young Dobbin when one of the youngsters of the school, having run into the town upon a poaching excursion for hardbake[2] and polonies,[3] espied the cart of Dobbin and Rudge, Grocers and Oilmen, Thames Street, London, at the Doctor's door, discharging a cargo of the wares in which the firm dealt.

Young Dobbin had no peace after that. The jokes were frightful, and merciless against him. 'Hullo, Dobbin,' one wag would say, 'here's good news in the paper. Sugar is ris', my boy.' Another would set a sum – 'If a pound of mutton-candles cost sevenpence-halfpenny, how much must Dobbin cost?' and a roar would follow from all the circle of young knaves, usher[4] and all, who rightly considered that the selling of goods by retail is a shameful and infamous practice, meriting the contempt and scorn of all real gentlemen.

'Your father's only a merchant, Osborne,' Dobbin said in private to the little boy who had brought down the storm upon him. At which the latter replied haughtily, 'My father's a gentleman, and keeps his carriage;' and Mr William Dobbin retreated to a remote outhouse in the playground, where he passed a half-holiday in the bitterest sadness and woe. Who amongst us is there that does not recollect similar hours of bitter, bitter childish grief? Who feels injustice; who shrinks before a slight; who has a sense of wrong so acute, and so glowing a gratitude of kindness, as a generous boy? and how many of those gentle souls do you degrade, estrange, torture, for the sake of a little loose arithmetic, and miserable dog-Latin.

Now, William Dobbin, from an incapacity to acquire

[2] toffee
[3] cooked sausages
[4] assistant teacher

the rudiments of the above language, as they are propounded in that wonderful book the Eton Latin Grammar, was compelled to remain among the very last of Dr Swishtail's scholars, and was 'taken down' continually by little fellows with pink faces and pinafores when he marched up with the lower form, a giant amongst them, with downcast stupefied look, his dog's-eared primer, and his tight corduroys. High and low, all made fun of him. They sewed up those corduroys, tight as they were. They cut his bed-strings. They upset buckets and benches, so that he might break his shins over them, which he never failed to do. They sent him parcels, which, when opened, were found to contain the paternal soap and candles. There was no little fellow but had his jeer and joke at Dobbin; and he bore everything quite patiently, and was entirely dumb and miserable.

Cuff, on the contrary, was the great chief and dandy of the Swishtail Seminary. He smuggled wine in. He fought the town-boys. Ponies used to come for him to ride home on Saturdays. He had his top-boots in his room, in which he used to hunt in the holidays. He had a gold repeater:[5] and took snuff like the Doctor. He had been to the Opera, and knew the merits of the principal actors, preferring Mr Kean to Mr Kemble. He could knock you off forty Latin verses in an hour. He could make French poetry. What else didn't he know, or couldn't he do? They said even the Doctor himself was afraid of him.

Cuff, the unquestioned king of the school, ruled over his subjects, and bullied them, with splendid superiority. This one blacked his shoes: that toasted his

[5] watch

bread, others would fag out,[6] and give him balls at cricket during whole summer afternoons. 'Figs' was the fellow whom he despised most, and with whom, though always abusing him, and sneering at him, he scarcely ever condescended to hold personal communication.

One day in private, the two young gentlemen had had a difference. Figs, alone in the school-room, was blundering over a home letter; when Cuff, entering, bade him go upon some message, of which tarts were probably the subject.

'I can't,' says Dobbin; 'I want to finish my letter.'

'You *can't!*' says Mr Cuff, laying hold of that document (in which many words were scratched out, many were misspelt, on which had been spent I don't know how much thought, and labour, and tears; for the poor fellow was writing to his mother, who was fond of him, although she was a grocer's wife, and lived in a back parlour in Thames Street). 'You *can't?*' says Mr Cuff: 'I should like to know why, pray? Can't you write to old Mother Figs tomorrow?'

'Don't call names,' Dobbin said, getting off the bench very nervous.

'Well, sir, will you go?' crowed the cock of the school.

'Put down the letter,' Dobbin replied; 'no gentleman readth letterth.'

'Well, *now* will you go?' says the other.

'No, I won't. Don't strike, or I'll *thmash* you,' roars out Dobbin, springing to a leaden inkstand, and looking so wicked, that Mr Cuff paused, turned down his coat sleeves again, put his hands into his pockets, and walked away with a sneer. But he never meddled personally with the grocer's boy after that; though we

---

[6] run errands, do household chores

must do him the justice to say he always spoke of Mr Dobbin with contempt behind his back.

Some time after this interview, it happened that Mr Cuff, on a sunshiny afternoon, was in the neighbourhood of poor William Dobbin, who was lying under a tree in the playground, spelling over a favourite copy of the *Arabian Nights* which he had – apart from the rest of the school, who were pursuing their various sports – quite lonely, and almost happy. If people would but leave children to themselves; if teachers would cease to bully them; if parents would not insist upon directing their thoughts, and dominating their feelings – those feelings and thoughts which are a mystery to all (for how much do you and I know of each other, of our children, of our fathers, of our neighbour, and how far more beautiful and sacred are the thoughts of the poor lad or girl whom you govern likely to be, than those of the dull and world-corrupted person who rules him?) – if, I say, parents and masters would leave their children alone a little more, – small harm would accrue, although a less quantity of *as in praesenti*[7] might be acquired.

Well, William Dobbin had for once forgotten the world, and was away with Sindbad the Sailor in the Valley of Diamonds, or with Prince Ahmed and the Fairy Peribanou in that delightful cavern where the Prince found her, and whither we should all like to make a tour; when shrill cries, as of a little fellow weeping, woke up his pleasant reverie; and looking up, he saw Cuff before him, belabouring a little boy.

It was the lad who had peached upon him about the grocer's cart; but he bore little malice, not at least towards the young and small. 'How dare you, sir, break

[7] a chapter in the Eton Latin Grammar

the bottle?' says Cuff to the little urchin, swinging a yellow cricket-stump over him.

The boy had been instructed to get over the playground wall (at a selected spot where the broken glass had been removed from the top, and niches made convenient in the brick); to run a quarter of a mile; to purchase a pint of rumshrub[8] on credit; to brave all the Doctor's outlying spies, and to clamber back into the playground again; during the performance of which feat, his foot had slipt, and the bottle was broken, and the shrub had been spilt, and his pantaloons had been damaged, and he appeared before his employer a perfectly guilty and trembling, though harmless, wretch.

'How dare you, sir, break it?' says Cuff; 'you blundering little thief. You drank the shrub, and now you pretend to have broken the bottle. Hold out your hand, sir.'

Down came the stump with a great heavy thump on the child's hand. A moan followed. Dobbin looked up. The Fairy Peribanou had fled into the inmost cavern with Prince Ahmed: the Roc had whisked away Sindbad the Sailor out of the Valley of Diamonds out of sight, far into the clouds: and there was everyday life before honest William; and a big boy beating a little one without cause.

'Hold out your other hand, sir,' roars Cuff to his little school-fellow, whose face was distorted with pain. Dobbin quivered, and gathered himself up in his narrow old clothes.

'Take that, you little devil!' cried Mr Cuff, and down came the wicket again on the child's hand. Don't be horrified, ladies, every boy at a public school has done

8 mixture of fruit juice and rum

it. Your children will so do and be done by, in all probability. Down came the wicket again; and Dobbin started
up.

I can't tell what his motive was. Torture in a public
school is as much licensed as the knout[9] in Russia. It
would be ungentlemanlike (in a manner) to resist it.
Perhaps Dobbin's foolish soul revolted against that
exercise of tyranny; or perhaps he had a hankering
feeling of revenge in his mind, and longed to measure
himself against that splendid bully and tyrant, who had
all the glory, pride, pomp, circumstance, banners
flying, drums beating, guards saluting, in the place.
Whatever may have been his incentive, however, up he
sprang, and screamed out, 'Hold off, Cuff; don't bully
that child any more; or I'll' –

'Or you'll what?' Cuff asked in amazement at this
interruption. 'Hold out your hand, you little beast.'

'I'll give you the worst thrashing you ever had in your
life,' Dobbin said, in reply to the first part of Cuff's
sentence; and little Osborne, gasping and in tears,
looked up with wonder and incredulity at seeing this
amazing champion put up suddenly to defend him:
while Cuff's astonishment was scarcely less. Fancy our
late monarch George III when he heard of the revolt of
the North American colonies: fancy brazen Goliath
when little David stepped forward and claimed a
meeting; and you have the feelings of Mr Reginald Cuff
when this rencontre was proposed to him.

'After school,' says he, of course; after a pause and a
look, as much as to say, 'Make your will, and communicate your last wishes to your friends between this time
and that.'

[9] whip

'As you please,' Dobbin said. 'You must be my bottle-holder, Osborne.'

'Well, if you like,' little Osborne replied; for you see his papa kept a carriage, and he was rather ashamed of his champion.

Yes, when the hour of battle came, he was almost ashamed to say, 'Go it, Figs;' and not a single other boy in the place uttered that cry for the first two or three rounds of this famous combat, at the commencement of which the scientific Cuff, with a contemptuous smile on his face, and as light and as gay as if he was at a ball, planted his blows upon his adversary, and floored that unlucky champion three times running. At each fall there was a cheer; and everybody was anxious to have the honour of offering the conqueror a knee.

'What a licking I shall get when it's over,' young Osborne thought, picking up his man. 'You'd best give in,' he said to Dobbin; 'it's only a thrashing, Figs, and you know I'm used to it.' But Figs, all whose limbs were in a quiver, and whose nostrils were breathing rage, put his little bottle-holder aside, and went in for a fourth time.

As he did not in the least know how to parry the blows that were aimed at himself, and Cuff had begun the attack on the three preceding occasions, without ever allowing his enemy to strike, Figs now determined that he would commence the engagement by a charge on his own part; and accordingly, being a left-handed man, brought that arm into action, and hit out a couple of times with all his might – once at Mr Cuff's left eye, and once on his beautiful Roman nose.

Cuff went down this time, to the astonishment of the assembly. 'Well hit, by Jove,' says little Osborne, with the air of a connoisseur, clapping his man on the back. 'Give it him with the left, Figs my boy.'

Figs' left made terrific play during all the rest of the combat. Cuff went down every time. At the sixth round, there were almost as many fellows shouting out, 'Go it, Figs,' as there were youths exclaiming, 'Go it, Cuff.' At the twelfth round the latter champion was all abroad, as the saying is, and had lost all presence of mind and power of attack or defence. Figs, on the contrary, was as calm as a Quaker. His face being quite pale, his eyes shining open, and a great cut on his under lip bleeding profusely, gave this young fellow a fierce and ghastly air, which perhaps struck terror into many spectators. Nevertheless, his intrepid adversary prepared to close for the thirteenth time.

If I had the pen of a Napier,[10] or a Bell's Life,[11] I should like to describe this combat properly. It was the last charge of the Guard – (that is, it *would* have been, only Waterloo had not yet taken place) – it was Ney's column breasting the hill of La Haye Sainte, bristling with ten thousand bayonets, and crowned with twenty eagles – it was the shout of the beef-eating British, as leaping down the hill they rushed to hug the enemy in the savage arms of battle – in other words, Cuff coming up full of pluck, but quite reeling and groggy, the Fig-merchant put in his left as usual on his adversary's nose, and sent him down for the last time.

'I think *that* will do for him,' Figs said, as his opponent dropped as neatly on the green as I have seen Jack Spot's ball plump into the pocket at billiards; and the fact is, when time was called, Mr Reginald Cuff was not able, or did not choose, to stand up again.

And now all the boys set up such a shout for Figs as

[10] author of *History of the Peninsular War*
[11] a London sporting magazine

would have made you think he had been their darling champion through the whole battle; and as absolutely brought Dr Swishtail out of his study, curious to know the cause of the uproar. He threatened to flog Figs violently, of course; but Cuff, who had come to himself by this time, and was washing his wounds, stood up and said, 'It's my fault, sir – not Figs' – not Dobbin's. I was bullying a little boy; and he served me right.' By which magnanimous speech he not only saved his conqueror a whipping, but got back all his ascendency over the boys which his defeat had nearly cost him.

I Remember

from *David Copperfield*

by Charles Dickens

David Copperfield tells us the story of his life. Here, he takes us back to his earliest memories of his childhood. He lives with his mother and their servant, Peggotty. One day, his mother arrives home with the sinister Mr Murdstone, who will later become David's stepfather.

The first objects that assume a distinct presence before me, as I look far back, into the blank of my infancy, are my mother with her pretty hair and youthful shape, and Peggotty with no shape at all, and eyes so dark that they seemed to darken their whole neighbourhood in her face, and cheeks and arms so hard and red that I wondered the birds didn't peck her in preference to apples.

I believe I can remember these two at a little distance apart, dwarfed to my sight by stooping down or kneeling on the floor, and I going unsteadily from the one to the other. I have an impression on my mind which I cannot distinguish from actual remembrance, of the touch of Peggotty's forefinger as she used to hold it out to me, and of its being roughened by needlework, like a pocket nutmeg-grater.

This may be fancy, though I think the memory of most of us can go farther back into such times than many of us suppose; just as I believe the power of observation in numbers of very young children to be quite wonderful for its closeness and accuracy. Indeed, I think that most grown men who are remarkable in this respect, may with greater propriety be said not to have lost the faculty, than to have acquired it; the rather, as I generally observe such men to retain a certain freshness, and gentleness, and capacity of being pleased, which are also an inheritance they have preserved from their childhood.

I might have a misgiving that I am 'meandering' in stopping to say this, but that it brings me to remark that I build these conclusions, in part upon my own experience of myself; and if it should appear from anything I may set down in this narrative that I was a child of close observation, or that as a man I have a strong memory of my childhood, I undoubtedly lay claim to both of these characteristics.

Looking back, as I was saying, into the blank of my infancy, the first objects I can remember as standing out by themselves from a confusion of things, are my mother and Peggotty. What else do I remember? Let me see.

There comes out of the cloud, our house – not new to me, but quite familiar, in its earliest remembrance. On the ground-floor is Peggotty's kitchen, opening into a back yard; with a pigeon-house on a pole, in the centre, without any pigeons in it; a great dog-kennel in a corner, without any dog; and a quantity of fowls that look terribly tall to me, walking about, in a menacing and ferocious manner. There is one cock who gets upon a post to crow, and seems to take particular notice of me as I look at him through the kitchen window, who makes me shiver, he is so fierce. Of the geese outside the side-gate who come waddling after me with their long necks stretched out when I go that way, I dream at night: as a man environed by wild beasts might dream of lions.

Here is a long passage – what an enormous perspective I make of it! – leading from Peggotty's kitchen to the front door. A dark store-room opens out of it, and that is a place to be run past at night; for I don't know what may be among those tubs and jars and old tea-chests, when there is nobody in there with a dimly-burning light, letting a mouldy air come out of the door, in which there is the smell of soap, pickles, pepper, candles, and coffee, all at one whiff. Then there are the two parlours: the parlour in which we sit of an evening, my mother and I and Peggotty – for Peggotty is quite our companion, when her work is done and we are alone – and the best parlour where we sit on a Sunday; grandly, but not so comfortably. There is something of a doleful air about that room to me, for Peggotty has told me – I don't know when, but apparently ages ago – about my father's funeral, and the company having their black cloaks put on. One Sunday night my mother reads to Peggotty and me in there, how Lazarus was raised up from the dead. And I am so frightened that they are afterwards obliged to take me out of bed, and shew me the quiet churchyard out of the bedroom window, with the dead all lying in their graves at rest, below the solemn moon.

There is nothing half so green that I know anywhere, as the grass of that churchyard; nothing half so shady as its trees; nothing half so quiet as its tombstones. The sheep are feeding there, when I kneel up, early in the morning, in my little bed in a closet within my mother's room, to look out at it; and I see the red light shining on the sun-dial, and think within myself, 'Is the sun-dial glad, I wonder, that it can tell the time again?'

Here is our pew in the church. What a high-backed pew! With a window near it, out of which our house can be seen, and *is* seen many times during the morning's service, by Peggotty, who likes to make herself as sure as she can that it's not being robbed, or is not in flames. But though Peggotty's eye wanders, she is much offended if mine does, and frowns to me, as I stand upon the seat, that I am to look at the clergyman. But I can't always look at him – I know him without that white thing on, and I am afraid of his wondering why I stare so, and perhaps stopping the service to inquire – and what am I to do? It's a dreadful thing to gape, but I must do something. I look at my mother, but *she* pretends not to see me. I look at a boy in the aisle, and *he* makes faces at me. I look at the sunlight coming in at the open door through the porch, and there I see a stray sheep – I don't mean a sinner, but mutton – half making up his mind to come into the church. I feel that if I looked at him any longer, I might be tempted to say something out loud; and what would become of me then! I look up at the monumental tablets on the wall, and try to think of Mr Bodgers late of this parish, and what the feelings of Mrs Bodgers must have been, when affliction sore, long time Mr Bodgers bore, and physicians were in vain. I wonder whether they called in Mr Chillip, and he was in vain; and if so, how he likes to be reminded of it once a week. I look from Mr Chillip, in his Sunday neckcloth, to the pulpit; and think what a good place it would be to play in, and what a castle it would make, with another boy coming up the stairs to attack it, and having the velvet cushion with the tassels thrown down on his head. In time my eyes gradually shut up; and, from seeming to hear the clergyman singing a drowsy song in the heat, I hear nothing, until I fall off the seat with a crash, and am taken out, more dead than alive, by Peggotty.

And now I see the outside of our house, with the latticed bedroom-windows standing open to let in the sweet-smelling air, and the ragged old rooks'-nests still dangling in the elm-trees at the bottom of the front garden. Now I am in the garden at the back, beyond the yard where the empty pigeon-house and dog-kennel are – a very preserve of butterflies, as I remember it, with a high fence, and a gate and padlock; where the fruit clusters on the trees, riper and richer than fruit has ever been since, in any other garden, and where my mother gathers some in a basket, while I stand by, bolting furtive gooseberries, and trying to look un-moved. A great wind rises, and the summer is gone in a moment. We are playing in the winter twilight, dancing about the parlour. When my mother is out of breath and rests herself in an elbow-chair, I watch her winding her bright curls round her fingers, and straitening her waist, and nobody knows better than I do that she likes to look so well, and is proud of being so pretty.

That is among my very earliest impressions. That, and a sense that we were both a little afraid of Peggotty, and submitted ourselves in most things to her direc-tion, were among the first opinions – if they may be so called – that I ever derived from what I saw.

Peggotty and I were sitting one night by the parlour fire, alone. I had been reading to Peggotty about croco-diles. I must have read very perspicuously, or the poor soul must have been deeply interested, for I remember she had a cloudy impression, after I had done, that they were a sort of vegetable. I was tired of reading, and dead sleepy; but having leave, as a high treat, to sit up until my mother came home from spending the evening at a neighbour's, I would rather have died upon my post (of course) than have gone to bed. I had reached that stage of sleepiness when Peggotty seemed to swell and grow immensely large. I propped my eyelids open with my two forefingers, and looked perseveringly at her as she sat at work; at the little bit of wax-candle she kept for her thread – how old it looked, being so wrinkled in all directions! – at the little house with a thatched roof, where the yard-measure lived; at her work-box with a sliding lid, with a view of St Paul's Cathedral (with a pink dome) painted on the top; at the brass thimble on her finger; at herself, whom I thought lovely. I felt so sleepy, that I knew if I lost sight of anything for a moment, I was gone.

'Peggotty,' says I, suddenly, 'were you ever married?'

'Lord, Master Davy,' replied Peggotty. 'What's put marriage in your head?'

She answered with such a start, that it quite awoke me. And then she stopped in her work, and looked at me, with her needle drawn out to its thread's length.

'But *were* you ever married, Peggotty?' says I. 'You are a very handsome woman, an't you?'

I thought her in a different style from my mother, certainly; but of another school of beauty, I considered her a perfect example. There was a red velvet footstool in the best parlour, on which my mother had painted a nosegay.[1] The ground-work of that stool, and Peggotty's complexion appeared to me to be one and the same thing. The stool was smooth, and Peggotty was rough, but that made no difference.

'Me handsome, Davy!' said Peggotty. 'Lawk, no, my dear! But what put marriage in your head?'

'I don't know! – You mustn't marry more than one person at a time, may you, Peggotty?'

'Certainly not,' says Peggotty, with the promptest decision.

'But if you marry a person, and the person dies, why

[1] bunch of flowers

then you may marry another person, mayn't you, Peggotty?'

'You MAY,' says Peggotty, 'if you choose, my dear. That's a matter of opinion.'

'But what is your opinion, Peggotty?' said I.

I asked her, and looked curiously at her, because she looked so curiously at me.

'My opinion is,' said Peggotty, taking her eyes from me, after a little indecision and going on with her work, 'that I never was married myself, Master Davy, and that I don't expect to be. That's all I know about the subject.'

'You an't cross, I suppose, Peggotty, are you?' said I, after sitting quiet for a minute.

I really thought she was, she had been so short with me; but I was quite mistaken: for she laid aside her work (which was a stocking of her own), and opening her arms wide, took my curly head within them, and gave it a good squeeze. I know it was a good squeeze, because, being very plump, whenever she made any little exertion after she was dressed, some of the buttons on the back of her gown flew off. And I recollect two bursting to the opposite side of the parlour, while she was hugging me.

'Now let me hear some more about the Crorkindills,' said Peggotty, who was not quite right in the name yet, 'for I an't heard half enough.'

I couldn't quite understand why Peggotty looked so queer, or why she was so ready to go back to the crocodiles. However, we returned to those monsters, with fresh wakefulness on my part, and we left their eggs in the sand for the sun to hatch; and we ran away from them, and baffled them by constantly turning, which they were unable to do quickly, on account of their unwieldy make; and we went into the water after them, as natives, and put sharp pieces of timber down their throats; and in short we ran the whole crocodile gauntlet. *I* did, at least; but I had my doubts of Peggotty, who was thoughtfully sticking her needle into various parts of her face and arms, all the time.

We had exhausted the crocodiles, and begun with the alligators, when the garden-bell rang. We went out to the door; and there was my mother, looking unusually pretty, I thought, and with her a gentleman with beautiful black hair and whiskers, who had walked home with us from church last Sunday.

As my mother stooped down on the threshold to take me in her arms and kiss me, the gentleman said I was a more highly privileged little fellow than a monarch – or something like that; for my later understanding comes, I am sensible, to my aid here.

'What does that mean?' I asked him, over her shoulder.

He patted me on the head; but somehow, I didn't like him or his deep voice, and I was jealous that his hand should touch my mother's in touching me – which it did. I put it away, as well as I could.

'Oh, Davy!' remonstrated my mother.

'Dear boy!' said the gentleman. 'I cannot wonder at his devotion!'

I never saw such a beautiful colour on my mother's face before. She gently chid me for being rude; and, keeping me close to her shawl, turned to thank the gentleman for taking so much trouble as to bring her home. She put her hand to him as she spoke, and, as he met it with his own, she glanced, I thought, at me.

'Let us say "good night", my fine boy,' said the gentleman, when he had bent his head – *I* saw him! – over my mother's little glove.

'Good night!' said I.

'Come! Let us be the best friends in the world!' said the gentleman, laughing, 'Shake hands!'

My right hand was in my mother's left, so I gave him the other.

'Why, that's the wrong hand, Davy!' laughed the gentleman.

My mother drew my right hand forward, but I was resolved, for my former reason, not to give it him, and I did not. I gave him the other, and he shook it heartily, and said I was a brave fellow, and went away.

At this minute I see him turn round in the garden, and give us a last look with his ill-omened black eyes, before the door was shut.

First Love

from *Villette*

by Charlotte Brontë

The narrator is Lucy Snowe, a young girl who prides herself on
her common sense and self-control. She is staying at the home
of her godmother, Mrs Bretton, and her sixteen-year-old son,
Graham. Mr Home, a family friend, has asked Mrs Bretton to
look after his little girl, Polly, while he goes away for a while.

On the morning of Mr Home's departure, he and his
daughter had some conversation in a window-recess by
themselves; I heard part of it.

'Couldn't I pack my box and go with you, papa?' she
whispered earnestly.

He shook his head.

'Should I be a trouble to you?'

'Yes, Polly.'

'Because I am little?'

'Because you are little and tender. It is only great,
strong people that should travel. But don't look sad, my
little girl; it breaks my heart. Papa will soon come back
to his Polly.'

'Indeed, indeed, I am not sad, scarcely at all.'

'Polly would be sorry to give papa pain; would she
not?'

'Sorrier than sorry.'

'Then Polly must be cheerful: not cry at parting; not
fret afterwards. She must look forward to meeting
again, and try to be happy meanwhile. Can she do this?'

'She will try.'

'I see she will. Farewell, then. It is time to go.'

'*Now?* – just *now?*'

'Just now.'

She held up quivering lips. Her father sobbed, but she, I remarked, did not. Having put her down, he shook hands with the rest present, and departed.

When the street-door closed, she dropped on her knees at a chair with a cry – 'Papa!'

It was low and long; a sort of 'Why hast thou forsaken me?' During an ensuing space of some minutes, I perceived she endured agony. She went through, in that brief interval of her infant life, emotions such as some never feel; it was in her constitution: she would have more of such instants if she lived. Nobody spoke. Mrs Bretton, being a mother, shed a tear or two. Graham, who was writing, lifted up his eyes and gazed at her. I, Lucy Snowe, was calm.

The little creature, thus left unharassed, did for herself what none other could do – contended with an intolerable feeling; and, ere long, in some degree, repressed it. That day she would accept solace from none; nor the next day: she grew more passive afterwards.

On the third evening, as she sat on the floor, worn and quiet, Graham, coming in, took her up gently, without a word. She did not resist: she rather nestled in his arms, as if weary. When he sat down, she laid her head against him; in a few minutes she slept; he carried her upstairs to bed. I was not surprised that, the next morning, the first thing she demanded was 'Where is Mr Graham?'

It happened that Graham was not coming to the breakfast-table; he had some exercises to write for that morning's class, and had requested his mother to send a cup of tea into the study. Polly volunteered to carry it:

she must be busy about something, look after somebody. The cup was entrusted to her: for, if restless, she
was also careful. As the study was opposite the breakfast-
room, the doors facing across the passage, my eye
followed her.

'What are you doing?' she asked, pausing on the
threshold.

'Writing,' said Graham.

'Why don't you come to take breakfast with your
mama?'

'Too busy.'

'Do you want any breakfast?'

'Of course.'

'There then.'

And she deposited the cup on the carpet, like a jailer
putting a prisoner's pitcher of water through his cell-
door, and retreated. Presently she returned.

'What will you have besides tea – what to eat?'

'Anything good. Bring me something particularly
nice; that's a kind little woman.'

She came back to Mrs Bretton.

'Please, ma'am, send your boy something good.'

'You shall choose for him, Polly; what shall my boy
have?'

She selected a portion of whatever was best on the
table, and ere long, came back with a whispered request
for some marmalade, which was not there. Having got
it, however (for Mrs Bretton refused the pair nothing),
Graham was shortly after heard lauding her to the skies;
promising that, when he had a house of his own, she
should be his housekeeper, and perhaps – if she showed
any culinary genius – his cook; and, as she did not
return, and I went to look after her, I found Graham
and her breakfasting *tête-à-tête* – she standing at his
elbow, and sharing his fare: excepting the marmalade,

which she delicately refused to touch; lest, I suppose, it should appear that she had procured it as much on her own account as his. She constantly evinced these nice perceptions and delicate instincts.

The league of acquaintanceship thus struck up was not hastily dissolved; on the contrary, it appeared that time and circumstances served rather to cement than loosen it. Ill-assimilated as the two were in age, sex, pursuits, &c., they somehow found a great deal to say to each other. As to Paulina, I observed that her little character never properly came out, except with young Bretton. As she got settled, and accustomed to the house, she proved tractable enough with Mrs Bretton; but she would sit on a stool at that lady's feet all day long, learning her task, or sewing, or drawing figures with a pencil on a slate, and never kindling once to originality, or showing a single gleam of the peculiarities of her nature. I ceased to watch her under such circumstances: she was not interesting. But the moment Graham's knock sounded of an evening, a change occurred; she was instantly at the head of the staircase. Usually her welcome was a reprimand or a threat.

'You have not wiped your shoes properly on the mat. I shall tell your mama.'

'Little busybody! Are you there?'

'Yes – and you can't reach me: I am higher up than you' (peeping between the rails of the bannister; she could not look over them).

'Polly!'

'My dear boy!' (such was one of her terms for him, adopted in imitation of his mother.)

'I am fit to faint with fatigue,' declared Graham, leaning against the passage-wall in seeming exhaustion. 'Dr Digby' (the headmaster) 'has quite knocked me up

with over-work. Just come down and help me to carry
up my book.'

'Ah! You're cunning!'

'Not at all, Polly – it is positive fact. I'm as weak as a
rush. Come down.'

'Your eyes are quiet like the cat's, but you'll spring.'

'Spring? Nothing of the kind: it isn't in me. Come
down.'

'Perhaps I may – if you'll promise not to touch – not
to snatch me up, and not to whirl me round.'

'I? I couldn't do it!' (sinking into a chair.)

'Then put the books down on the first step, and go
three yards off.'

This being done, she descended warily, and not
taking her eyes from the feeble Graham. Of course her
approach always galvanised him to new and spasmodic
life: the game of romps was sure to be exacted.
Sometimes she would be angry; sometimes the matter
was allowed to pass smoothly, and we could hear her say
as she led him upstairs:

'Now, my dear boy, come and take your tea – I am
sure you must want something.'

It was sufficiently comical to observe her as she sat
beside Graham, while he took that meal. In his absence
she was a still personage, but with him the most
officious, fidgetty little body possible. I often wished she
would mind herself and be tranquil; but no – herself
was forgotten in him: he could not be sufficiently well
waited on, nor carefully enough looked after; he was
more than the Grand Turk[1] in her estimation. . . .

The pair seldom quarrelled; yet once a rupture
occurred, in which her feelings received a severe shock.

[1] the Ottoman sultan

One day Graham, on the occasion of his birthday, had some friends – lads of his own age – to dine with him. Paulina took much interest in the coming of these friends; she had frequently heard of them; they were amongst those of whom Graham oftenest spoke. After dinner, the young gentlemen were left by themselves in the dining-room, where they soon became very merry and made a good deal of noise. Chancing to pass through the hall, I found Paulina sitting alone on the lowest step of the staircase, her eyes fixed on the glossy panels of the dining-room door, where the reflection of the hall-lamp was shining; her little brow knit in anxious meditation.

'What are you thinking about, Polly?'

'Nothing particular; only I wish that door was clear glass – that I might see through it. The boys seem very cheerful, and I want to go to them: I want to be with Graham, and watch his friends.'

'What hinders you from going?'

'I feel afraid: but may I try, do you think? May I knock at the door, and ask to be let in?'

I thought perhaps they might not object to have her as a playmate, and therefore encouraged the attempt.

She knocked – too faintly at first to be heard, but on a second essay the door unclosed; Graham's head appeared; he looked in high spirits but impatient.

'What do you want, you little monkey?'

'To come to you.'

'Do you indeed? As if I would be troubled with you! Away to mama and Mistress Snowe, and tell them to put you to bed.' The auburn head and bright flushed face vanished, – the door shut peremptorily. She was stunned.

'Why does he speak so? He never spoke so before,' she said in consternation. 'What have I done?'

'Nothing, Polly; but Graham is busy with his school-friends.'

'And he likes them better than me! He turns me away now they are here!'

I had some thoughts of consoling her, and of improving the occasion by inculcating some of those maxims of philosophy whereof I had ever a tolerable stock ready for application. She stopped me, however, by putting her fingers in her ears at the first words I uttered, and then lying down on the mat with her face against the flags; nor could either Warren or the cook root her from that position: she was allowed to lie, therefore, till she chose to rise of her own accord.

Graham forgot his impatience the same evening, and would have accosted her as usual when his friends were gone, but she wrenched herself from his hand; her eye quite flashed; she would not bid him goodnight; she would not look in his face. The next day he treated her with indifference, and she grew like a bit of marble. The day after, he teased her to know what was the matter; her lips would not unclose. Of course he could not feel real anger on his side: the match was too unequal in every way; he tried soothing and coaxing. 'Why was she angry? What had he done?' By-and-by tears answered him; he petted her and they were friends. But she was one on whom such incidents were not lost: I remarked that never after this rebuff did she seek him, or follow him, or in any way solicit his notice. I told her once to carry a book or some other article to Graham when he was shut up in his study.

'I shall wait till he comes out,' said she, proudly; 'I don't choose to give him the trouble of rising to open the door.'

Young Bretton had a favourite pony on which he often rode out; from the window she always watched his departure and return. It was her ambition to be permitted to have a ride round the courtyard on this pony; but far be it from her to ask such a favour. One day she descended to the yard to watch him dismount; as she leaned against the gate, the longing wish for the indulgence of a ride glittered in her eye.

'Come, Polly, will you have a canter?' asked Graham half carelessly. I suppose she thought he was *too* careless.

'No thank you,' said she, turning away with the utmost coolness.

'You'd better;' pursued he. 'You will like it, I am sure.'

'Don't think I should care a fig about it,' was the response.

'That is not true. You told Lucy Snowe you longed to have a ride.'

'Lucy Snowe is a *tatter*-box,' I heard her say: (her imperfect articulation was the least precocious thing she had about her), and with this, she walked into the house. Graham coming in soon after, observed to his mother –

'Mama, I believe that creature is a changeling: she is a perfect cabinet of oddities; but I should be dull without her: she amuses me a great deal more than you or Lucy Snowe.'

'Miss Snowe,' said Paulina to me (she had now got into the habit of occasionally chatting with me when we were alone in our room at night), 'do you know on what day in the week I like Graham best?'

'How can I possibly know anything so strange? Is there one day out of the seven when he is otherwise than on the other six?'

'To be sure! Can't you see? Don't you know? I find him the most excellent on a Sunday; then we have him the whole day, and he is quiet, and, in the evening, *so* kind.'

This observation was not altogether groundless: going to church, &c., kept Graham quiet on the Sunday, and the evening he generally dedicated to a serene, though rather indolent sort of enjoyment by the parlour fireside. He would take possession of the couch, and then he would call Polly.

Graham was a boy not quite as other boys are; all his delight did not lie in action: he was capable of some intervals of contemplation; he could take a pleasure too in reading, nor was his selection of books wholly indiscriminate: there were glimmerings of characteristic preference and even of instinctive taste in the choice. He rarely, it is true, remarked on what he read, but I have seen him sit and think of it.

Polly, being near him, kneeling on a little cushion or the carpet, a conversation would begin in murmurs, not inaudible, though subdued. I caught a snatch of their tenor now and then; and, in truth, some influence better and finer than that of every day, seemed to soothe Graham at such times into no ungentle mood.

'Have you learned any hymns this week, Polly?'

'I have learned a very pretty one, four verses long. Shall I say it?'

'Speak nicely, then: don't be in a hurry.'

The hymn being rehearsed, or rather half-chanted, in a little singing voice, Graham would take exceptions at the manner, and proceed to give a lesson in recitation. She was quick in learning, apt in imitating; and, besides, her pleasure was to please Graham: she proved a ready scholar. To the hymn would succeed some reading – perhaps a chapter in the Bible; correction was seldom required here, for the child could read any simple narrative chapter very well; and, when the subject was such as she could understand and take an interest in, her expression and emphasis were something remarkable. Joseph cast into the pit; the calling of Samuel; Daniel in the lion's den; – these were favourite passages: of the first especially she seemed perfectly to feel the pathos.

'Poor Jacob!' she would sometimes say, with quivering lips. 'How he loved his son Joseph! As much,' she once added – 'as much, Graham, as I love you: if you were to die' (and she re-opened the book, sought the verse, and read), 'I should "refuse to be comforted, and go down into the grave to your mourning."'

With these words she gathered Graham in her little arms, drawing his long-tressed head towards her. The action, I remember, struck me as strangely rash; exciting the feeling one might experience on seeing an animal dangerous by nature, and but half-tamed by art, too heedlessly fondled. Not that I feared Graham would hurt, or very roughly check her; but I thought she ran risk of incurring such a careless, impatient repulse, as would be worse almost to her than a blow. On the whole, however, these demonstrations were borne passively: sometimes even a sort of complacent wonder at her earnest partiality would smile not unkindly in his eyes. Once he said:

'You like me almost as well as if you were my little sister, Polly.'

'Oh, I *do* like you,' said she; 'I *do* like you very much.'

A Naughty Girl

from *The Mill on the Floss*

by George Eliot

Maggie Tulliver and her brother, Tom, are visiting their uncle
and aunt Pullet. Maggie, already in trouble for cutting off all
her long hair in a fit of rebellion, gets into more trouble on this
visit. She becomes jealous of the attention her beloved Tom is
paying to their cousin Lucy and takes her revenge.

The startling object which thus made an epoch for
uncle Pullet was no other than little Lucy, with one side
of her person, from her small foot to her bonnet-crown,
wet and discoloured with mud, holding out two tiny
blackened hands and making a very piteous face. To
account for this unprecedented apparition in aunt
Pullet's parlour, we must return to the moment when
the three children went to play out of doors and the
small demons who had taken possession of Maggie's
soul at an early period of the day had returned in all the
greater force after a temporary absence. All the disagreeable recollections of the morning were thick upon
her, when Tom, whose displeasure towards her had
been considerably refreshed by her foolish trick of
causing him to upset his cowslip wine, said, 'Here, Lucy,
you come along with me,' and walked off to the area
where the toads were, as if there were no Maggie in
existence. Seeing this Maggie lingered at a distance
looking like a small Medusa[1] with her snakes cropped.

[1] a monster in Greek myth whose hair consisted of live serpents

Lucy was naturally pleased that cousin Tom was so good to her, and it was very amusing to see him tickling a fat toad with a piece of string when the toad was safe down the area with an iron grating over him. Still Lucy wished Maggie to enjoy the spectacle also, especially as she would doubtless find a name for the toad and say what had been his past history; for Lucy had a delighted semi-belief in Maggie's stories about the live things they came upon by accident – how Mrs Earwig had a wash at home, and one of her children had fallen into the hot copper, for which reason, she was running so fast to fetch the doctor. Tom had a profound contempt for this nonsense of Maggie's, smashing the earwig at once as a superfluous yet easy means of proving the entire unreality of such a story; but Lucy, for the life of her, could not help fancying there was something in it, and at all events thought it was very pretty make-believe. So now the desire to know the history of a very portly toad, added to her habitual affectionateness, made her run back to Maggie and say, 'O, there is such a big, funny toad, Maggie! Do come and see.'

Maggie said nothing, but turned away from her with a deeper frown. As long as Tom seemed to prefer Lucy to her, Lucy made part of his unkindness. Maggie would have thought a little while ago that she could never be cross with pretty little Lucy, any more than she could be cruel to a little white mouse; but then, Tom had always been quite indifferent to Lucy before, and it had been left to Maggie to pet and make much of her. As it was, she was actually beginning to think that she should like to make Lucy cry, by slapping or pinching her, especially as it might vex Tom, whom it was of no use to slap even if she dared, because he didn't mind it. And if Lucy hadn't been there, Maggie was sure he would have got friends with her sooner.

Tickling a fat toad who is not highly sensitive is an amusement that it is possible to exhaust, and Tom by-and-by began to look round for some other mode of passing the time. But in so prim a garden where they were not to go off the paved walks, there was not a great choice of sport. The only great pleasure such a restriction allowed was the pleasure of breaking it, and Tom began to meditate an insurrectionary visit to the pond, about a field's length beyond the garden.

'I say, Lucy,' he began, nodding his head up and down with great significance as he coiled up his string again. 'What do you think I mean to do?'

'What, Tom?' said Lucy, with curiosity.

'I mean to go to the pond, and look at the pike. You may go with me if you like,' said the young Sultan.

'O, Tom, *dare* you?' said Lucy. 'Aunt said we mustn't go out of the garden.'

'O, I shall go out at the other end of the garden,' said Tom. 'Nobody 'ull see us. Besides I don't care if they do – I'll run off home.'

'But *I* couldn't run,' said Lucy, who had never before been exposed to such severe temptation.

'O, never mind – they won't be cross with *you*,' said Tom. 'You say I took you.'

Tom walked along, and Lucy trotted by his side timidly enjoying the rare treat of doing something naughty – excited also by the mention of that celebrity, the pike, about which she was quite uncertain whether it was a fish or a fowl. Maggie saw them leaving the garden, and could not resist the impulse to follow. Anger and jealousy can no more bear to lose sight of their objects than love, and that Tom and Lucy should do or see anything of which she was ignorant would have been an intolerable idea to Maggie. So she kept a few yards behind them, unobserved by Tom, who was presently absorbed in watching for the 'jack-pike' – a highly interesting monster – he was said to be so very old, so very large, and to have such a remarkable appetite. The pike, like other celebrities did not show when he was watched for, but Tom caught sight of something in rapid movement in the water which attracted him to another spot on the brink of the pond.

'Here, Lucy!' he said in a loud whisper, 'come here! Take care! Keep on the grass – don't step where the cows have been!' he added pointing to a peninsula of dry grass, with trodden mud on each side of it; for Tom's contemptuous conception of a girl included the attribute of being unfit to walk in dirty places.

Lucy came carefully as she was bidden, and bent down to look at what seemed a golden arrow-head darting through the water. It was a water-snake, Tom told her, and Lucy at last could see the serpentine wave of its body, very much wondering that a snake could swim. Maggie had drawn nearer and nearer – she *must* see it too, though it was bitter to her like everything else, since Tom did not care about her seeing it. At last, she was close by Lucy, and Tom, who had been aware of her approach, but would not notice it till he was obliged, turned round and said,

'Now, get away, Maggie. There's no room for you on the grass here. Nobody asked *you* to come.'

There were passions at war in Maggie at that moment to have made a tragedy, if tragedies were made by passion only, but the essential τι μεγεθοσ[2] which was present in the passion, was wanting to the action; the

---

[2] a reference to Aristotle's definition of tragedy as having a certain *magnitude*. This magnitude is present in Maggie's feelings but not in her actions, which are anything but heroic.

utmost Maggie could do, with a fierce thrust of her small brown arm, was to push poor little pink-and-white Lucy into the cow-trodden mud.

Then Tom could not restrain himself, and gave Maggie two smart slaps on the arm as he ran to pick up Lucy, who lay crying helplessly. Maggie retreated to the roots of a tree a few yards off and looked on impenitently. Usually her repentance came quickly after one rash deed, but now Tom and Lucy had made her so miserable, she was glad to spoil their happiness – glad to make everybody uncomfortable. Why should she be sorry? – Tom was very slow to forgive *her*, however sorry she might have been.

'I shall tell mother, you know, Miss Mag,' said Tom, loudly and emphatically, as soon as Lucy was up and ready to walk away. It was not Tom's practice to 'tell,' but here justice clearly demanded that Maggie should be visited with the utmost punishment: not that Tom had learnt to put his views in that abstract form; he never mentioned 'justice,' and had no idea that his desire to punish might be called by that fine name. Lucy was too entirely absorbed by the evil that had befallen her – the spoiling of her pretty best clothes, and the discomfort of being wet and dirty – to think much of the cause, which was entirely mysterious to her. She could never have guessed what she had done to make Maggie angry with her. But she felt that Maggie was very unkind and disagreeable, and made no magnanimous entreaties to Tom that he would not 'tell,' only running along by his side and crying piteously, while Maggie sat on the roots of the tree and looked after them with her small Medusa face.

'Sally,' said Tom, when they reached the kitchen door, and Sally looked at them in speechless amaze, with a piece of bread-and-butter in her mouth and a toasting-fork in her hand, 'Sally, tell mother it was Maggie pushed Lucy into the mud.'

'But Lors ha'massy, how did you get near such mud as that?' said Sally, making a wry face, as she stooped down and examined the *corpus delicti*.[3]

Tom's imagination had not been rapid and capacious enough to include this question among the foreseen consequences, but it was no sooner put than he foresaw whither it tended, and that Maggie would not be considered the only culprit in the case. He walked quietly away from the kitchen door, leaving Sally to that pleasure of guessing which active minds notoriously prefer to ready-made knowledge.

Sally, as you are aware, lost no time in presenting Lucy at the parlour door, for to have so dirty an object introduced into the house at Garum Firs was too great a weight to be sustained by a single mind.

'Goodness gracious!' aunt Pullet exclaimed after preluding by an inarticulate scream. 'Keep her at the door, Sally! Don't bring her off the oilcloth, whatever you do.'

'Why, she's tumbled into some nasty mud,' said Mrs Tulliver, going up to Lucy to examine into the amount of damage to clothes for which she felt herself responsible to her sister Deane.

'If you please, 'um, it was Miss Maggie as pushed her in,' said Sally. 'Master Tom's been and said so. And they must ha' been to the pond, for it's only there they could ha' got into such dirt.'

'There it is, Bessy – it's what I've been telling you,' said Mrs Pullet, in a tone of prophetic sadness, 'it's your children – there's no knowing what they'll come to.'

Mrs Tulliver was mute, feeling herself a truly

---

[3] the body of evidence that shows that a crime has been committed

wretched mother. As usual, the thought pressed upon her that people would think she had done something wicked to deserve her maternal troubles, while Mrs Pullet began to give elaborate directions to Sally how to guard the premises from serious injury in the course of removing the dirt. Meantime tea was to be brought in by the cook, and the two naughty children were to have theirs in an ignominious manner in the kitchen. Mrs Tulliver went out to speak to these naughty children, supposing them to be close at hand, but it was not until after some search that she found Tom leaning with rather a hardened careless air against the white paling of the poultry yard, and lowering his piece of string on the other side as a means of exasperating the turkey cock.

'Tom, you naughty boy, where's your sister?' said Mrs Tulliver, in a distressed voice.

'I don't know,' said Tom. His eagerness for justice on Maggie had diminished since he had seen clearly that it could hardly be brought about without the injustice of some blame on his own conduct.

'Why, where did you leave her?' said his mother, looking round.

'Sitting under the tree against the pond,' said Tom, apparently indifferent to everything but the string and the turkey cock.

'Then go and fetch her in this minute, you naughty boy. And how could you think o' going to the pond, and taking your sister where there was dirt? You know she'll do mischief if there's mischief to be done.'

It was Mrs Tulliver's way, if she blamed Tom, to refer his misdemeanour, somehow or other, to Maggie.

The idea of Maggie sitting alone by the pond, roused an habitual fear in Mrs Tulliver's mind, and she mounted the horse-block to satisfy herself by a sight of that fatal child, while Tom walked – not very quickly – on his way towards her.

'They're such children for the water, mine are,' she said aloud, without reflecting that there was no one to hear her. 'They'll be brought in dead and drownded some day. I wish that river was far enough.'

But when she not only failed to discern Maggie, but presently saw Tom returning from the pool alone, this hovering fear entered and took complete possession of her, and she hurried to meet him.

'Maggie's nowhere about the pond, mother,' said Tom, 'she's gone away.'

You may conceive the terrified search for Maggie, and the difficulty of convincing her mother that she was not in the pond. Mrs Pullet observed, that the child might come to a worse end if she lived – there was no knowing; and Mr Pullet, confused and overwhelmed by this revolutionary aspect of things – the tea deferred and the poultry alarmed by the unusual running to and fro – took up his spud as an instrument of search, and reached down a key to unlock the goose-pen, as a likely place for Maggie to lie perdue[4] in.

Tom, after a while, started the idea that Maggie was gone home (without thinking it necessary to state that it was what he should have done himself under the circumstances), and the suggestion was seized as a comfort by his mother.

'Sister, for goodness' sake, let 'em put the horse in the carriage and take me home – we shall perhaps find her on the road. Lucy can't walk in her dirty clothes,' she said, looking at that innocent victim, who was

[4] lost, hidden (from the French)

wrapped up in a shawl and sitting with naked feet on the sofa.

Aunt Pullet was quite willing to take the shortest means of restoring her premises to order and quiet, and it was not long before Mrs Tulliver was in the chaise looking anxiously at the most distant point before her. What the father would say if Maggie was lost? was a question that predominated over every other.

The Mysterious Count Fosco

from *The Woman in White*

by Wilkie Collins

Marian Halcombe, the unusual, sharp-witted heroine, is
describing the mysterious Count Fosco. The Count and his
wife have come to stay at Blackwater Park, the home of Sir
Percival Glyde. Marian's half-sister, Laura, is Sir Percival's new
bride. She has brought Marian to stay at Blackwater Park to be
her companion. Marian keeps a private journal of what she
observes at Blackwater Park.

What of the Count?

This in two words: He looks like a man who could
tame anything. If he had married a tigress, instead of a
woman, he would have tamed the tigress. If he had
married *me*, I should have made his cigarettes, as his
wife does – I should have held my tongue when he
looked at me, as she holds hers.

I am almost afraid to confess it, even to these secret
pages. The man has interested me, has attracted me,
has forced me to like him. In two short days he has
made his way straight into my favourable estimation,
and how he has worked the miracle is more than I can
tell.

It absolutely startles me, now he is in my mind, to
find how plainly I see him – how much more plainly
than I see Sir Percival, or Mr Fairlie, or Walter
Hartright, or any other absent person of whom I think,
with the one exception of Laura herself! I can hear his
voice, as if he was speaking at this moment. I know what

his conversation was yesterday, as well as if I was hearing it now. How am I to describe him? There are peculiarities in his personal appearance, his habits, and his amusements, which I should blame in the boldest terms, or ridicule in the most merciless manner, if I had seen them in another man. What is it that makes me unable to blame them, or to ridicule them in *him*?

For example, he is immensely fat. Before this time I have always especially disliked corpulent humanity. I have always maintained that the popular notion of connecting excessive grossness of size and excessive good-humour as inseparable allies was equivalent to declaring, either that no people but amiable people ever get fat, or that the accidental addition of so many pounds of flesh has a directly favourable influence over the disposition of the person on whose body they accumulate. I have invariably combated both these absurd assertions by quoting examples of fat people who were as mean, vicious, and cruel as the leanest and the worst of their neighbours. I have asked whether Henry the Eighth was an amiable character? Whether Pope Alexander the Sixth was a good man? Whether Mr Murderer and Mrs Murderess Manning were not both unusually stout people? Whether hired nurses, proverbially as cruel a set of women as are to be found in all England, were not, for the most part, also as fat a set of women as are to be found in all England?[1] and so on, through dozens of other examples, modern and ancient, native and foreign, high and low. Holding these strong opinions on the subject with might and main as I do at this moment, here, nevertheless, is Count Fosco, as fat as Henry the Eighth himself, estab-

---

[1] Before Florence Nightingale reformed nursing conditions, hired nurses were notorious for cruelty and drunkenness.

lished in my favour, at one day's notice, without let or hindrance from his own odious corpulence. Marvellous indeed!

Is it his face that has recommended him?

It may be his face. He is a most remarkable likeness, on a large scale, of the great Napoleon. His features have Napoleon's magnificent regularity – his expression recalls the grandly calm, immovable power of the Great Soldier's face. This striking resemblance certainly impressed me, to begin with; but there is something in him besides the resemblance, which has impressed me more. I think the influence I am now trying to find is in his eyes. They are the most unfathomable grey eyes I ever saw, and they have at times a cold, clear, beautiful, irresistible glitter in them which forces me to look at him, and yet causes me sensations, when I do look, which I would rather not feel. Other parts of his face and head have their strange peculiarities. His complexion, for instance, has a singular sallow-fairness, so much at variance with the dark-brown colour of his hair, that I suspect the hair of being a wig, and his face, closely shaven all over, is smoother and freer from all marks and wrinkles than mine, though (according to Sir Percival's account of him) he is close on sixty years of age. But these are not the prominent personal characteristics which distinguish him, to my mind, from all the other men I have ever seen. The marked peculiarity which singles him out from the rank and file of humanity lies entirely, so far as I can tell at present, in the extraordinary expression and extraordinary power of his eyes.

His manner and his command of our language may also have assisted him, in some degree, to establish himself in my good opinion. He has that quiet deference, that look of pleased, attentive interest in listening to a woman, and that secret gentleness in his voice in speaking to a woman, which, say what we may, we can none of us resist. . . .

All the smallest characteristics of this strange man have something strikingly original and perplexingly contradictory in them. Fat as he is and old as he is, his movements are astonishingly light and easy. He is as noiseless in a room as any of us women, and more than that, with all his look of unmistakable mental firmness and power, he is as nervously sensitive as the weakest of us. He starts at chance noises as inveterately as Laura herself. He winced and shuddered yesterday, when Sir Percival beat one of the spaniels, so that I felt ashamed of my own want of tenderness and sensibility by comparison with the Count.

The relation of this last incident reminds me of one of his most curious peculiarities, which I have not yet mentioned – his extraordinary fondness for pet animals.

Some of these he has left on the Continent, but he has brought with him to this house a cockatoo, two canary-birds, and a whole family of white mice. He attends to all the necessities of these strange favourites himself, and he has taught the creatures to be surprisingly fond of him and familiar with him. The cockatoo, a most vicious and treacherous bird towards every one else, absolutely seems to love him. When he lets it out of its cage, it hops on to his knee, and claws its way up his great big body, and rubs its top-knot against his sallow double chin in the most caressing manner imaginable. He has only to set the doors of the canaries' cages open, and to call them, and the pretty little cleverly trained creatures perch fearlessly on his hand, mount his fat outstretched fingers one by one, when he tells them to 'go upstairs', and sing together as if they would burst their throats with delight when they get to the top finger. His white mice live in a little pagoda of gaily painted wirework, designed and made by himself. They are almost as tame as the canaries, and they are perpetually let out like the canaries. They crawl all over him, popping in and out of his waistcoat, and sitting in couples, white as snow, on his capacious shoulders. He seems to be even fonder of his mice than of his other pets, smiles at them, and kisses them, and calls them by all sorts of endearing names. If it be possible to suppose an Englishman with any taste for such childish interests and amusements as these, that Englishman would certainly feel rather ashamed of them, and would be anxious to apologise for them, in the company of grown-up people. But the Count, apparently, sees nothing ridiculous in the amazing contrast between his colossal self and his frail little pets. He would blandly kiss his white mice and twitter to his canary-birds amid an assembly of English fox-hunters, and would only pity them as barbarians when they were all laughing their loudest at him.

It seems hardly credible while I am writing it down, but it is certainly true, that this same man, who has all the fondness of an old maid for his cockatoo, and all the small dexterities of an organ-boy in managing his white mice, can talk, when anything happens to rouse him, with a daring independence of thought, a knowledge of books in every language, and an experience of society in half the capitals of Europe, which would make him the prominent personage of any assembly in the civilised world. This trainer of canary-birds, this architect of a pagoda for white mice, is (as Sir Percival himself has told me) one of the first experimental chemists living, and has discovered, among other wonderful inventions, a means of petrifying the body after death, so as to preserve it, as hard as marble, to the end of time. This fat, indolent, elderly man, whose nerves are so finely strung that he starts at chance noises, and winces when he sees a house-spaniel get a whipping, went into the stable-yard on the morning after his arrival, and put his hand on the head of a chained bloodhound – a beast so savage that the very groom who feeds him keeps out of his reach. His wife and I were present, and I shall not forget the scene that followed, short as it was.

'Mind that dog, sir,' said the groom; 'he flies at every body!' 'He does that, my friend,' replied the Count quietly, 'because everybody is afraid of him. Let us see if he flies at *me*.' And he laid his plump, yellow-white fingers, on which the canary-birds had been perching ten minutes before, upon the formidable brute's head, and looked him straight in the eyes. 'You big dogs are all cowards,' he said, addressing the animal contemptuously, with his face and the dog's within an inch of each other. 'You would kill a poor cat, you infernal coward. You would fly at a starving beggar, you infernal coward. Anything that you can surprise unawares – anything that is afraid of your big body, and your wicked white teeth, and your slobbering, bloodthirsty mouth, is the thing you like to fly at. You could throttle me at this moment, you mean, miserable bully, and you daren't so much as look me in the face, because I'm not afraid of you. Will you think better of it, and try your teeth in my fat neck? Bah! not you!' He turned away, laughing at the astonishment of the men in the yard, and the dog crept back meekly to his kennel. 'Ah! my nice waist-coat!' he said pathetically. 'I am sorry I came here. Some of that brute's slobber has got on my pretty clean waistcoat.' Those words express another of his incomprehensible oddities. He is as fond of fine clothes as the veriest fool in existence, and has appeared in four magnificent waistcoats already – all of light garish colours, and all immensely large even for him – in the two days of his residence at Blackwater Park.

His tact and cleverness in small things are quite as noticeable as the singular inconsistencies in his character, and the childish triviality of his ordinary tastes and pursuits.

I can see already that he means to live on excellent terms with all of us during the period of his sojourn in this place. He has evidently discovered that Laura secretly dislikes him (she confessed as much to me when I pressed her on the subject) – but he has also found out that she is extravagantly fond of flowers. Whenever she wants a nosegay he has got one to give her, gathered and arranged by himself, and greatly to my amusement, he is always cunningly provided with a duplicate, composed of exactly the same flowers, grouped in exactly the same way, to appease his icily jealous wife before she can so much as think herself aggrieved. His management of the Countess (in public) is a sight to see. He bows to her, he habitually addresses her as 'my angel,' he carries his canaries to pay her little visits on his fingers and to sing to her, he kisses her hand when she gives him his cigarettes; he presents her with sugar-plums in return, which he puts into her mouth playfully, from a box in his pocket. The rod of iron with which he rules her never appears in company – it is a private rod, and is always kept upstairs.

Wife for Sale!

from *The Mayor of Casterbridge*

by Thomas Hardy

In this, the opening chapter, we meet Michael Henchard, later
to become the mayor of the title, and his wife Susan. The
young couple, looking for work and a place to live, arrive at a
country fair.

One evening of late summer, before the nineteenth
century had reached one-third of its span, a young man
and woman, the latter carrying a child, were approaching the large village of Weydon-Priors, in Upper
Wessex, on foot. They were plainly but not ill clad,
though the thick hoar of dust which had accumulated
on their shoes and garments from an obviously long
journey lent a disadvantageous shabbiness to their
appearance just now.

The man was of fine figure, swarthy, and stern in
aspect; and he showed in profile a facial angle so
slightly inclined as to be almost perpendicular. He wore
a short jacket of brown corduroy, newer than the
remainder of his suit, which was a fustian waistcoat with
white horn buttons, breeches of the same, tanned
leggings, and a straw hat overlaid with black glazed
canvas. At his back he carried by a looped strap a rush
basket, from which protruded at one end the crutch of
a hay-knife, a wimble[1] for hay-bonds being also visible in
the aperture. His measured, springless walk was the

[1] an instrument for twisting the bands which bound hay trusses

walk of the skilled countryman as distinct from the desultory shamble of the general labourer; while in the turn and plant of each foot there was, further, a dogged and cynical indifference personal to himself, showing its presence even in the regularly interchanging fustian folds, now in the left leg, now in the right, as he paced along.

What was really peculiar, however, in this couple's progress, and would have attracted the attention of any casual observer otherwise disposed to overlook them, was the perfect silence they preserved. They walked side by side in such a way as to suggest afar off the low, easy, confidential chat of people full of reciprocity; but on closer view it could be discerned that the man was reading, or pretending to read, a ballad sheet which he kept before his eyes with some difficulty by the hand that was passed through the basket strap. Whether this apparent cause were the real cause, or whether it were an assumed one to escape an intercourse that would have been irksome to him, nobody but himself could have said precisely; but his taciturnity was unbroken, and the woman enjoyed no society whatever from his presence. Virtually she walked the highway alone, save for the child she bore. Sometimes the man's bent elbow almost touched her shoulder, for she kept as close to his side as was possible without actual contact; but she seemed to have no idea of taking his arm, nor he of offering it; and far from exhibiting surprise at his ignoring silence she appeared to receive it as a natural thing. If any word at all were uttered by the little group, it was an occasional whisper of the woman to the child – a tiny girl in short clothes and blue boots of knitted yarn – and the murmured babble of the child in reply. . . .

The trusser and his family proceeded on their way,

and soon entered the Fair-field, which showed standing-places and pens where many hundreds of horses and sheep had been exhibited and sold in the forenoon, but were now in great part taken away. At present, as their informant had observed, but little real business remained on hand, the chief being the sale by auction of a few inferior animals, that could not otherwise be disposed of, and had been absolutely refused by the better class of traders, who came and went early. Yet the crowd was denser now than during the morning hours, the frivolous contingent of visitors, including journey-men out for a holiday, a stray soldier or two come on furlough, village shopkeepers, and the like, having latterly flocked in; persons whose activities found a congenial field among the peep-shows, toy-stands, waxworks, inspired monsters, disinterested medical men who travelled for the public good, thimble-riggers,[2] nick-nack vendors, and readers of Fate.

Neither of our pedestrians had much heart for these things, and they looked around for a refreshment tent among the many which dotted the down. Two, which stood nearest to them in the ochreous haze of expiring sunlight, seemed almost equally inviting. One was formed of new, milk-hued canvas, and bore red flags on its summit; it announced 'Good Home-brewed Beer, Ale, and Cyder.' The other was less new; a little iron stove-pipe came out of it at the back, and in front appeared the placard, 'Good Furmity Sold Hear.' The man mentally weighed the two inscriptions, and inclined to the former tent.

'No – no – the other one,' said the woman. 'I always like furmity; and so does Elizabeth-Jane; and so will you. It is nourishing after a long hard day.'

2 cheats

'I've never tasted it,' said the man. However, he gave way to her representations, and they entered the furmity booth forthwith.

A rather numerous company appeared within, seated at the long narrow tables that ran down the tent on each side. At the upper end stood a stove, containing a charcoal fire, over which hung a large three-legged crock, sufficiently polished round the rim to show that it was made of bell-metal. A haggish creature of about fifty presided, in a white apron, which, as it threw an air of respectability over her as far as it extended, was made so wide as to reach nearly round her waist. She slowly stirred the contents of the pot. The dull scrape of her large spoon was audible throughout the tent as she thus kept from burning the mixture of corn in the grain, flour, milk, raisins, currants, and what not, that composed the antiquated slop in which she dealt. Vessels holding the separate ingredients stood on a white-clothed table of boards and trestles close by.

The young man and woman ordered a basin each of the mixture, steaming hot, and sat down to consume it at leisure. This was very well so far, for furmity, as the woman had said, was nourishing, and as proper a food as could be obtained within the four seas; though, to those not accustomed to it, the grains of wheat swollen as large as lemon-pips, which floated on its surface, might have a deterrent effect at first.

But there was more in that tent than met the cursory glance; and the man, with the instinct of a perverse character, scented it quickly. After a mincing attack on his bowl, he watched the hag's proceedings from the corner of his eye, and saw the game she played. He winked to her, and passed up his basin in reply to her nod; when she took a bottle from under the table, slily measured out a quantity of its contents, and tipped the same into the man's furmity. The liquor poured in was rum. The man as slily sent back money in payment.

He found the concoction, thus strongly laced, much more to his satisfaction than it had been in its natural state. His wife had observed the proceeding with much uneasiness; but he persuaded her to have hers laced also, and she agreed to a milder allowance after some misgiving.

The man finished his basin, and called for another, the rum being signalled for in yet stronger proportion. The effect of it was soon apparent in his manner, and his wife but too sadly perceived that in strenuously steering off the rocks of the licensed liquor-tent she had only got into maelstrom depths here amongst the smugglers.

The child began to prattle impatiently, and the wife more than once said to her husband, 'Michael, how about our lodging? You know we may have trouble in getting it if we don't go soon.'

But he turned a deaf ear to those bird-like chirpings. He talked loud to the company. The child's black eyes, after slow, round, ruminating gazes at the candles when they were lighted, fell together; then they opened, then shut again, and she slept.

At the end of the first basin the man had risen to serenity; at the second he was jovial; at the third, argumentative; at the fourth, the qualities signified by the shape of his face, the occasional clench of his mouth, and the fiery spark of his dark eye, began to tell in his conduct; he was overbearing – even brilliantly quarrelsome.

The conversation took a high turn, as it often does on such occasions. The ruin of good men by bad wives, and, more particularly, the frustration of many a promising youth's high aims and hopes and the extinction of his energies by an early imprudent marriage, was the theme.

'I did for myself that way thoroughly,' said the trusser, with a contemplative bitterness that was well-nigh resentful. 'I married at eighteen, like the fool that I was; and this is the consequence o't.' He pointed at himself and family with a wave of the hand intended to bring out the penuriousness of the exhibition.

The young woman his wife, who seemed accustomed to such remarks, acted as if she did not hear them, and continued her intermittent private words on tender trifles to the sleeping and waking child, who was just big enough to be placed for a moment on the bench beside her when she wished to ease her arms. The man continued –

'I haven't more than fifteen shillings in the world, and yet I am a good experienced hand in my line. I'd challenge England to beat me in the fodder business; and if I were a free man again I'd be worth a thousand pound before I'd done o't. But a fellow never knows these little things till all chance of acting upon 'em is past.'

The auctioneer selling the old horses in the field outside could be heard saying, 'Now this is the last lot – now who'll take the last lot for a song? Shall I say forty shillings? 'Tis a very promising brood-mare, a trifle over five years old, and nothing the matter with the hoss at all, except that she's a little holler in the back and had her left eye knocked out by the kick of another, her own sister, coming along the road.'

'For my part I don't see why men who have got wives and don't want 'em shouldn't get rid of 'em as these gipsy fellows do their old horses,' said the man in the tent. 'Why shouldn't they put 'em up and sell 'em by auction to men who are in need of such articles? Hey?

Why, begad, I'd sell mine this minute if anybody would buy her!'

'There's them that would do that,' some of the guests replied, looking at the woman, who was by no means ill-favoured.

'True,' said a smoking gentleman, whose coat had the fine polish about the collar, elbows, seams, and shoulder-blades that long-continued friction with grimy surfaces will produce, and which is usually more desired on furniture than on clothes. From his appearance he had possibly been in former time groom or coachman to some neighbouring county family. 'I've had my breedings in as good circles, I may say, as any man,' he added, 'and I know true cultivation, or nobody do; and I can declare she's got it – in the bone, mind ye, I say – as much as any female in the fair – though it may want a little bringing out.' Then, crossing his legs, he resumed his pipe with a nicely-adjusted gaze at a point in the air.

The fuddled young husband stared for a few seconds at this unexpected praise of his wife, half in doubt of the wisdom of his own attitude towards the possessor of such qualities. But he speedily lapsed into his former conviction, and said harshly –

'Well, then, now is your chance; I am open to an offer for this gem o' creation.'

She turned to her husband and murmured, 'Michael, you have talked this nonsense in public places before. A joke is a joke, but you may make it once too often, mind!'

'I know I've said it before; I meant it. All I want is a buyer.'

At the moment a swallow, one among the last of the season, which had by chance found its way through an opening into the upper part of the tent, flew to and fro in quick curves above their heads, causing all eyes to follow it absently. In watching the bird till it made its escape the assembled company neglected to respond to the workman's offer, and the subject dropped.

But a quarter of an hour later the man, who had gone on lacing his furmity more and more heavily, though he was either so strong-minded or such an intrepid toper that he still appeared fairly sober, recurred to the old strain, as in a musical fantasy the instrument fetches up the original theme. 'Here – I am waiting to know about this offer of mine. The woman is no good to me. Who'll have her?'

The company had by this time decidedly degener-ated, and the renewed inquiry was received with a laugh of appreciation. The woman whispered; she was imploring and anxious: 'Come, come, it is getting dark, and this nonsense won't do. If you don't come along, I shall go without you. Come!'

She waited and waited; yet he did not move. In ten minutes the man broke in upon the desultory conversa-tion of the furmity drinkers with, 'I asked this question, and nobody answered to 't. Will any Jack Rag or Tom Straw among ye buy my goods?'

The woman's manner changed, and her face assumed the grim shape and colour of which mention has been made.

'Mike, Mike,' said she; 'this is getting serious. O! – too serious!'

'Will anybody buy her?' said the man.

'I wish somebody would,' said she firmly. 'Her present owner is not at all to her liking!'

'Nor you to mine,' said he. 'So we are agreed about that. Gentlemen, you hear? It's an agreement to part. She shall take the girl if she wants to, and go her ways. I'll take my tools, and go my ways. 'Tis simple as

127

Scripture history. Now then, stand up, Susan, and show yourself.'

'Don't, my chiel,' whispered a buxom staylace dealer in voluminous petticoats, who sat near the woman; 'yer good man don't know what he's saying.'

The woman, however, did stand up. 'Now, who's auctioneer?' cried the hay-trusser.

'I be,' promptly answered a short man, with a nose resembling a copper knob, a damp voice, and eyes like buttonholes. 'Who'll make an offer for this lady?'

The woman looked on the ground, as if she maintained her position by a supreme effort of will.

'Five shillings,' said some one, at which there was a laugh.

'No insults,' said the husband. 'Who'll say a guinea?'

Nobody answered; and the female dealer in staylaces interposed.

'Behave yerself moral, good man, for Heaven's love! Ah, what a cruelty is the poor soul married to! Bed and board is dear at some figures, 'pon my 'vation 'tis!'

'Set it higher, auctioneer,' said the trusser.

'Two guineas!' said the auctioneer; and no one replied.

'If they don't take her for that, in ten seconds they'll have to give more,' said the husband. 'Very well. Now, auctioneer, add another.'

'Three guineas – going for three guineas!' said the rheumy man.

'No bid?' said the husband. 'Good Lord, why she's cost me fifty times the money, if a penny. Go on.'

'Four guineas!' cried the auctioneer.

'I'll tell ye what – I won't sell her for less than five,' said the husband, bringing down his fist so that the basins danced. 'I'll sell her for five guineas to any man that will pay me the money, and treat her well; and he shall have her for ever, and never hear aught o' me. But she shan't go for less. Now then – five guineas – and she's yours. Susan, you agree?'

She bowed her head with absolute indifference.

'Five guineas,' said the auctioneer, 'or she'll be withdrawn. Do anybody give it? The last time. Yes or no?'

'Yes,' said a loud voice from the doorway.

All eyes were turned. Standing in the triangular opening which formed the door of the tent was a sailor, who, unobserved by the rest, had arrived there within the last two or three minutes. A dead silence followed his affirmation.

'You say you do?' asked the husband, staring at him.

'I say so,' replied the sailor.

'Saying is one thing, and paying is another. Where's the money?'

The sailor hesitated a moment, looked anew at the woman, came in, unfolded five crisp pieces of paper, and threw them down upon the table-cloth. They were Bank-of-England notes for five pounds. Upon the face of this he chinked down the shillings severally – one, two, three, four, five.

The sight of real money in full amount, in answer to a challenge for the same till then deemed slightly hypothetical, had a great effect upon the spectators. Their eyes became riveted upon the faces of the chief actors, and then upon the notes as they lay, weighted by the shillings, on the table.

Up to this moment it could not positively have been asserted that the man, in spite of his tantalising declaration, was really in earnest. The spectators had indeed taken the proceedings throughout as a piece of mirthful irony carried to extremes; and had assumed that, being out of work, he was, as a consequence, out of temper with the world, and society, and his nearest kin. But with the demand and response of real cash the jovial frivolity of the scene departed. A lurid colour seemed to fill the tent, and change the aspect of all therein. The mirth-wrinkles left the listeners' faces, and they waited with parting lips.

'Now,' said the woman, breaking the silence, so that her low dry voice sounded quite loud, 'before you go further, Michael, listen to me. If you touch that money, I and this girl go with the man. Mind, it is a joke no longer.'

'A joke? Of course it is not a joke!' shouted her husband, his resentment rising at her suggestion. 'I take the money: the sailor takes you. That's plain enough. It has been done elsewhere – and why not here?'

''Tis quite on the understanding that the young woman is willing,' said the sailor blandly. 'I wouldn't hurt her feelings for the world.'

'Faith, nor I', said her husband. 'But she is willing, provided she can have the child. She said so only the other day when I talked o't!'

'That you swear?' said the sailor to her.

'I do,' said she, after glancing at her husband's face and seeing no repentance there.

'Very well, she shall have the child, and the bargain's complete,' said the trusser. He took the sailor's notes and deliberately folded them, and put them with the shillings in a high remote pocket, with an air of finality.

The sailor looked at the woman and smiled. 'Come along!' he said kindly. 'The little one too – the more the merrier!' She paused for an instant, with a close glance at him. Then dropping her eyes again, and saying nothing, she took up the child and followed him as he made towards the door. On reaching it, she turned, and pulling off her wedding-ring, flung it across the booth in the hay-trusser's face.

'Mike,' she said, 'I've lived with thee a couple of years, and had nothing but temper! Now I'm no more to 'ee; I'll try my luck elsewhere. 'Twill be better for me and Elizabeth-Jane, both. So good-bye!'

Seizing the sailor's arm with her right hand, and mounting the little girl on her left, she went out of the tent sobbing bitterly.

A stolid look of concern filled the husband's face, as if, after all, he had not quite anticipated this ending; and some of the guests laughed.

'Is she gone?' he said.

'Faith, ay; she's gone clane enough,' said some rustics near the door.

A Terrifying Transformation

from *The Strange Case of Dr Jekyll and Mr Hyde*

by Robert Louis Stevenson

Dr Jekyll is a highly respected London doctor, who has begun to behave rather oddly. Dr Lanyon is a colleague of his. Lanyon is writing to a friend, Dr Utterson, to tell him about the strange letter he has received from Dr Jekyll and the visit from sinister Mr Hyde that followed. At the end of the extract, Lanyon refers to the murder of Sir Danvers Carew, a crime that has shocked the whole of London with its brutality.

On the ninth of January, now four days ago, I received by the evening delivery a registered envelope, addressed in the hand of my colleague and old school-companion, Henry Jekyll. I was a good deal surprised by this; for we were by no means in the habit of correspondence; I had seen the man, dined with him, indeed, the night before; and I could imagine nothing in our intercourse that should justify the formality of registration. The contents increased my wonder; for this is how the letter ran:

10*th December* 18—

DEAR LANYON

– You are one of my oldest friends; and although we may have differed at times on scientific questions, I cannot remember, at least on my side, any break in our affection. There was never a day when, if you had said to me, 'Jekyll, my life, my honour, my reason, depend upon you,' I would not have sacrificed my fortune or my left hand to help you. Lanyon, my life, my honour, my reason, are all at your mercy; if you fail me tonight, I am lost. You might suppose, after this preface, that I am going to ask you for something dishonourable to grant. Judge for yourself.

I want you to postpone all other engagements for tonight – ay, even if you were summoned to the bedside of an emperor; to take a cab, unless your carriage should be actually at the door; and, with this letter in your hand for consultation, to drive straight to my house. Poole, my butler, has his orders; you will find him waiting your arrival with a locksmith. The door of my cabinet is then to be forced; and you are to go in alone; to open the glazed press (letter E) on the left hand, breaking the lock if it be shut; and to draw out, *with all its contents as they stand*, the fourth drawer from the top or (which is the same thing) the third from the bottom. In my extreme distress of mind, I have a morbid fear of misdirecting you; but even if I am in error, you may know the right drawer by its contents: some powders, a phial,[1] and a paper book. This drawer I beg of you to carry back with you to Cavendish Square exactly as it stands.

That is the first part of the service: now for the second. You should be back, if you set out at once on the receipt of this, long before midnight; but I will leave you that amount of margin, not only in the fear of one of those obstacles that can neither be prevented nor foreseen, but because an hour when your servants are in bed is to be preferred for what will then remain to do. At midnight, then, I have to ask you to be alone in your consulting-room, to admit

---

[1] small glass bottle

with your own hand into the house a man who will present himself in my name, and to place in his hands the drawer that you will have brought with you from my cabinet. Then you will have played your part, and earned my gratitude completely. Five minutes afterwards, if you insist upon an explanation, you will have understood that these arrangements are of capital importance; and that by the neglect of one of them, fantastic as they must appear, you might have charged your conscience with my death or the shipwreck of my reason.

Confident as I am that you will not trifle with this appeal, my heart sinks and my hand trembles at the bare thought of such a possibility. Think of me at this hour, in a strange place, labouring under a blackness of distress that no fancy can exaggerate, and yet well aware that, if you will but punctually serve me, my troubles will roll away like a story that is told. Serve me, my dear Lanyon, and save

Your friend,
H. J. . . .

Upon the reading of this letter, I made sure my colleague was insane, but till that was proved beyond the possibility of doubt, I felt bound to do as he requested. The less I understood of this farrago, the less I was in a position to judge of its importance; and an appeal so worded could not be set aside without a grave responsibility. I rose accordingly from table, got into a hansom, and drove straight to Jekyll's house. The butler was awaiting my arrival; he had received by the same post as mine a registered letter of instruction, and had sent at once for a locksmith and a carpenter. The tradesmen came while we were yet speaking; and we moved in a body to old Dr Denman's surgical theatre, from which (as you are doubtless aware) Jekyll's private cabinet is most conveniently entered. The door was very strong, the lock excellent; the carpenter avowed he would have great trouble, and have to do much damage, if force were to be used; and the locksmith was near despair. But this last was a handy fellow, and after two hours' work, the door stood open. The press marked E was unlocked; and I took out the drawer, had it filled up with straw and tied in a sheet, and returned with it to Cavendish Square.

Here I proceeded to examine its contents. The powders were neatly enough made up, but not with the nicety of the dispensing chemist; so that it was plain they were of Jekyll's private manufacture; and when I opened one of the wrappers, I found what seemed to me a simple crystalline salt of a white colour. The phial, to which I next turned my attention, might have been about half full of a blood-red liquor, which was highly pungent to the sense of smell, and seemed to me to contain phosphorus and some volatile ether. At the other ingredients I could make no guess. The book was an ordinary version book, and contained little but a series of dates. These covered a period of many years; but I observed that the entries ceased nearly a year ago, and quite abruptly. Here and there a brief remark was appended to a date, usually no more than a single word: 'double' occurring perhaps six times in a total of several hundred entries; and once very early in the list, and followed by several marks of exclamation, 'total failure!!!' All this, though it whetted my curiosity, told me little that was definite. Here were a phial of some tincture, a paper of some salt, and the record of a series of experiments that had led (like too many of Jekyll's investigations) to no end of practical usefulness. How could the presence of these articles in my house affect either the honour, the sanity, or the life of my flighty colleague? If his messenger could go to one place, why could he not go to another? And even granting some impediment, why was this gentleman to be received by me in secret? The more I reflected, the more convinced I grew that I was dealing with a case of cerebral disease; and though I dismissed my servants to bed, I loaded an old revolver, that I might be found in some posture of self-defence.

Twelve o'clock had scarce rung out over London, ere the knocker sounded very gently on the door. I went myself at the summons, and found a small man crouching against the pillars of the portico.

'Are you come from Dr Jekyll?' I asked.

He told me 'yes' by a constrained gesture; and when I had bidden him enter, he did not obey me without a searching backward glance into the darkness of the square. There was a policeman not far off, advancing with his bull's-eye[2] open; and at the sight, I thought my visitor started and made greater haste.

These particulars struck me, I confess, disagreeably; and as I followed him into the bright light of the consulting-room, I kept my hand ready on my weapon. Here, at last, I had a chance of clearly seeing him. I had never set eyes on him before, so much was certain. He was small, as I have said; I was struck besides with the shocking expression of his face, with his remarkable combination of great muscular activity and great apparent debility of constitution, and – last but not least – with the odd, subjective disturbance caused by his neighbourhood. This bore some resemblance to incipient rigor, and was accompanied by a marked sinking of

[2] lantern

the pulse. At the time, I set it down to some idiosyn-
cratic, personal distaste, and merely wondered at the
acuteness of the symptoms; but I have since had reason
to believe the cause to lie much deeper in the nature of
man, and to turn on some nobler hinge than the
principle of hatred.

This person (who had thus, from the first moment of
his entrance, struck in me what I can only describe as a
disgustful curiosity) was dressed in a fashion that would
have made an ordinary person laughable; his clothes,
that is to say, although they were of rich and sober
fabric, were enormously too large for him in every
measurement – the trousers hanging on his legs and
rolled up to keep them from the ground, the waist of
the coat below his haunches, and the collar sprawling
wide upon his shoulders. Strange to relate, this
ludicrous accoutrement was far from moving me to
laughter. Rather, as there was something abnormal and
misbegotten in the very essence of the creature that
now faced me – something seizing, surprising and
revolting – this fresh disparity seemed but to fit in with
and to reinforce it; so that to my interest in the man's
nature and character there was added a curiosity as to
his origin, his life, his fortune and status in the world.

These observations, though they have taken so great
a space to be set down in, were yet the work of a few
seconds. My visitor was, indeed, on fire with sombre
excitement.

'Have you got it?' he cried. 'Have you got it?' And so
lively was his impatience that he even laid his hand
upon my arm and sought to shake me.

I put him back, conscious at his touch of a certain icy
pang along my blood. 'Come, sir,' said I. 'You forget
that I have not yet the pleasure of your acquaintance.
Be seated, if you please.' And I showed him an

example, and sat down myself in my customary seat and with as fair an imitation of my ordinary manner to a patient as the lateness of the hour, the nature of my preoccupations, and the horror I had of my visitor would suffer me to muster.

'I beg your pardon, Dr Lanyon,' he replied, civilly enough. 'What you say is very well founded; and my impatience has shown its heels to my politeness. I come here at the instance of your colleague, Dr Henry Jekyll, on a piece of business of some moment; and I understood . . .' he paused and put his hand to his throat, and I could see, in spite of his collected manner, that he was wrestling against the approaches of the hysteria – 'I understood, a drawer . . .'

But here I took pity on my visitor's suspense, and some perhaps on my own growing curiosity.

'There it is, sir,' said I, pointing to the drawer, where it lay on the floor behind a table, and still covered with the sheet.

He sprang to it, and then paused, and laid his hand upon his heart; I could hear his teeth grate with the convulsive action of his jaws; and his face was so ghastly to see that I grew alarmed both for his life and reason.

'Compose yourself,' said I.

He turned a dreadful smile to me, and, as if with the decision of despair, plucked away the sheet. At sight of the contents, he uttered one loud sob of such immense relief that I sat petrified. And the next moment, in a voice that was already fairly well under control, 'Have you a graduated glass?'[3] he asked.

I rose from my place with something of an effort, and gave him what he asked.

He thanked me with a smiling nod, measured out a

---

[3] measuring-glass

few minims of the red tincture and added one of the powders. The mixture, which was at first of a reddish hue, began, in proportion as the crystals melted, to brighten in colour, to effervesce audibly, and to throw off small fumes of vapour. Suddenly, and at the same moment, the ebullition ceased, and the compound changed to a dark purple, which faded again more slowly to a watery green. My visitor, who had watched these metamorphoses with a keen eye, smiled, set down the glass upon the table, and then turned and looked upon me with an air of scrutiny.

'And now,' said he, 'to settle what remains. Will you be wise? will you be guided? will you suffer me to take this glass in my hand, and to go forth from your house without further parley? or has the greed of curiosity too much command of you? Think before you answer, for it shall be done as you decide. As you decide, you shall be left as you were before, and neither richer nor wiser, unless the sense of service rendered to a man in mortal distress may be counted as a kind of riches of the soul. Or, if you shall so prefer to choose, a new province of knowledge and new avenues to fame and power shall be laid open to you, here, in this room, upon the instant; and your sight shall be blasted by a prodigy to stagger the unbelief of Satan.'

'Sir,' said I, affecting a coolness that I was far from truly possessing, 'you speak enigmas, and you will perhaps not wonder that I hear you with no very strong impression of belief. But I have gone too far in the way of inexplicable services to pause before I see the end.'

'It is well,' replied my visitor. 'Lanyon, you remember your vows: what follows is under the seal of our profession. And now, you who have so long been bound to the most narrow and material views, you who have denied the virtue of transcendental medicine, you who have derided your superiors – behold!'

He put the glass to his lips, and drank at one gulp. A cry followed; he reeled, staggered, clutched at the table and held on, staring with injected eyes, gasping with open mouth; and as I looked, there came, I thought, a change – he seemed to swell – his face became suddenly black, and the features seemed to melt and alter – and the next moment I had sprung to my feet and leaped back against the wall, my arm raised to shield me from that prodigy, my mind submerged in terror.

'O God!' I screamed, and 'O God!' again and again; for there before my eyes – pale and shaken, and half fainting, and groping before him with his hands, like a man restored from death – there stood Henry Jekyll!

What he told me in the next hour I cannot bring my mind to set on paper. I saw what I saw, I heard what I heard, and my soul sickened at it; and yet, now when that sight has faded from my eyes I ask myself if I believe it, and I cannot answer. My life is shaken to its roots; sleep has left me, the deadliest terror sits by me at all hours of the day and night; I feel that my days are numbered, and that I must die; and yet I shall die incredulous. As for the moral turpitude that man unveiled to me, even with tears of penitence, I cannot, even in memory, dwell on it without a start of horror. I will say but one thing, Utterson, and that (if you can bring your mind to credit it) will be more than enough. The creature who crept into my house that night was, on Jekyll's own confession, known by the name of Hyde and hunted for in every corner of the land as the murderer of Carew.

HASTIE LANYON

Study activities

Journey through Danger

1 *The Pilgrim's Progress* is allegorical. The main character, Christian, is making a journey through the world. Christian is a symbol of the human soul and the journey he makes is a symbol of life itself. What do the following characters and places represent: Lord Hategood, Mr Blind-man, Mr Liar, Mr Cruelty, Vanity-Fair, the Valley of the Shadow of Death?

2 However, *The Pilgrim's Progress* is more than just an allegory. In places, it is more like a novel. Christian and Faithful are more than symbols. They are almost real characters. Are you moved by anything in this extract? e.g. the friendship between Christian and Faithful? Faithful's death? Look at the description of Christian's race to beat Faithful, and his humiliation when he falls over. Discuss whether this is part of the allegory.

3 Write an episode to follow this extract in which Christian travels back through the Valley of the Shadow of Death with a new group of characters. One of them is called Cowardice. You can choose your own names for the others.

Shipwrecked

1 *Robinson Crusoe* is not an allegory. Make a two-column table showing the differences between *Robinson Crusoe* and *The Pilgrim's Progress* under the headings 'Names', 'Settings', 'Events', 'Feelings', and 'Moral?' Explain what makes *Robinson Crusoe* a novel rather than an allegory.

2 Daniel Defoe based *Robinson Crusoe* on the story of a real castaway, Alexander Selkirk. Imagine that you are the first newspaper reporter to have interviewed Robinson Crusoe on his return home and write your report of his story. Include a map of his island.

Diaries and letters

1 Samuel Richardson uses 'epistolary form' in his novel *Pamela*. 'Epistolary form' means writing a novel in the form of a series of letters ('epistle' = letter). Discuss how the use of letters allows us to learn about Pamela's thoughts and feelings.

2 Pamela has to cope with dangers from the outside and from within herself. Make a list of all these dangers. Write a letter to Pamela advising her on how to cope with some of these dangers.

3 Fanny Burney uses a similar form in her novel *Evelina*. A letter that has been left out of this extract describes Evelina's first walk in a London park and her first view of Buckingham Palace. Write the letter in which she describes these events, bringing out her excitement at being in a big city for the first time.

4 Write a series of letters between Pamela and Evelina in which Pamela gives some advice to Evelina about how to handle embarrassing young men, and Evelina tries to cheer up Pamela with gossip and cheerful news.

5 *The Woman in White* by Wilkie Collins is a much later novel. It is partly written in the form of Marian Halcombe's diary. In what ways is a novel in the form of a diary similar to an epistolary novel? In what ways is it different?

6 What can we tell about Marian Halcombe's feelings and attitudes? What does she think about Count Fosco and his wife? Does she seem to be confused about anything? How can you tell?

7 Later in the novel, we discover that Count Fosco is a criminal. Write the police description of him as a 'Wanted' man.

8 Devise a role-play in which you interview Countess Fosco about her husband.

9 What other novels have you read in which the writers use either letters or diaries to reveal the thoughts and feelings of their characters? Write a comparison of any two of these.

10 Write a story in epistolary form or using a mixture of letters and diaries.

Childhood

Charles Dickens was only one of many nineteenth-century writers who were interested in portraying the childhood of their characters. He was influenced by a group of early nineteenth-century poets and writers, known as the 'Romantics', who believed that childhood was a very special and significant time.

1 In *David Copperfield*, Dickens uses first person narrative ('I') to tell the story as though David Copperfield were remembering his own childhood. What are the earliest things that David can remember?

2 Dickens uses the present tense for some of David's memories. Collect some examples of this. Why does Dickens do this? How does Dickens suggest to us that David is a small boy and that he is still very innocent?

3 'Pathos' is the technique of making you feel pity for a character. Humour makes you see the funny side. Make a two-column table of any examples of pathos and humour you can find in this extract.

4 What does Dickens want us to think about the gentleman caller? How can you tell? Write a letter from David to Peggotty in which he confides in her his feelings about Mr Murdstone.

5 Recount your own earliest memories. Use first person narrative and some of Dickens's other techniques to write about them so that you make your reader feel as though they are seeing the world through a child's eyes. (You can make up the memories if you prefer.)

6 In *Wuthering Heights*, Emily Brontë introduces us to her two main characters, Cathy and Heathcliff, as children. How does Cathy change in this extract?

7 Heathcliff is a complex character who can arouse both sympathy and dislike in the reader. How does Emily Brontë encourage you to feel sympathy for him? Write an account of the Linton children's visit to Wuthering Heights from his point of view.

8 Charlotte Brontë, Emily's sister, also portrays the childhood of her characters in *Villette*. What is your opinion of the friendship between Polly and Graham?

9 Examine the characters of Polly and Lucy Snowe. Make a chart showing the differences between them. Account for the friendship between them.

10 Maggie in George Eliot's *The Mill on the Floss* is another child with very strong feelings. How does George Eliot help us to understand what Maggie is feeling?

11 Write a comparison between Maggie and Heathcliff, showing the reasons for their naughtiness and explaining whether you feel sympathy for them.

The subconscious mind

1 *The Castle of Otranto* by Horace Walpole was one of the most popular of the Gothic novels written in the eighteenth century. Gothic novels were concerned with horror, mystery and the supernatural. Writers of these novels tried to create an atmosphere of terror and emotional violence.

Describe the setting in this extract. How successful is it in creating a frightening atmosphere?

2 In the nineteenth century, many writers looked back to the Gothic novels to find images and symbols for the unconscious feelings and motives of their characters. R.L. Stevenson provides a good example of this in *The Strange Case of Dr Jekyll and Mr Hyde*. Make a chart showing the supernatural and horror elements in this story. What do you think that Stevenson is trying to show us about Dr Jekyll?

3 Which contemporary horror films or books do you think use mystery, terror or the supernatural to say something about the human subconscious?

4 Write a story using the same basic idea as the Jekyll and Hyde story. Your main character is haunted by a secret other side that they can no longer control. It could, for example, be a super athlete haunted by an *alter ego* who is lazy and a cheat, or a ruthless criminal whose other side is a complete softy.

Comedy and caricature

Many writers are more interested in the outer personality and physical appearance of their characters than in their unconscious mind, particularly writers who want to achieve a comic effect. Henry Fielding and Laurence Sterne were two eighteenth-century novelists who used the technique of 'caricature' to make their characters funny. A caricature is a character who is exaggerated to the point of being unbelievable and ridiculous. It is rather similar to the technique used by cartoonists. Fielding, however, defended himself from the charge of caricature by insisting that all his characters were based on human nature.

1 Make a table of the exaggerations in the descriptions of Squire Western in *Tom Jones* and Dr Slop in *The Life and Opinions of Tristram Shandy*. Are either of these characters believable as 'real people'? Which of the two do you find more humorous? Why?

2 Choose a well-known person and try writing a caricature yourself. See if anyone else can guess the identity of your caricature.

3 Some writers create comic characters in order to laugh at something in society that makes them angry or that they think is ridiculous. This kind of humour is known as satire or satirical comedy.

In *Northanger Abbey*, Jane Austen ridicules her two young heroines. What is she criticising about their behaviour and attitudes? Which of the two is made to look more ridiculous?

4 In *Vanity Fair*, Thackeray creates some comic characters to express some strong feelings. What is being laughed at? Who is being criticised? What is Thackeray angry about?

5 Write a comparison of any three characters from these extracts, giving your reasons for finding them funny or ridiculous.

6 Invent your own comic character and storyboard a series of comic adventures or mishaps in which your character's folly is exposed.

Wife for Sale!

1 Thomas Hardy has created an unusual character in Michael Henchard. Is there anything you like about him? Anything you don't like? Are you curious about anything?

2 Make detailed notes about Michael Henchard under the following headings: his appearance, his relationship with the woman and child, his weaknesses and strengths, his ambitions and worries. Find a quotation to go under each heading.

3 At what point does Henchard seriously decide to sell his wife? What makes him decide? How does this incident affect your response to Henchard? What attitude does Hardy encourage us to have towards Henchard?

4 Use the material and ideas you have collected so far to write a character study of Henchard.

Comparing characters

1 Compare different villains, selecting material from *The Castle of Otranto*, *The Woman in White* and *Dr Jekyll and Mr Hyde*.

2 Compare the different ways in which male–female relationships are portrayed, selecting material from *Evelina*, *Northanger Abbey*, *Villette*, *The Mill on the Floss*, *The Woman in White* or *The Mayor of Casterbridge*.

3 Compare the depiction of brothers and sisters, selecting material from *Tom Jones*, *Wuthering Heights* and *The Mill on the Floss*.

4 Compare characters who have to fight for their survival in some way, selecting material from *Robinson Crusoe*, *Pamela*, *The Castle of Otranto*, *Wuthering Heights* or *Dr Jekyll and Mr Hyde*.

5 Compare characters who are narrators, selecting material from *Robinson Crusoe*, *Pamela*, *Evelina*, *David Copperfield*, *Villette*, *The Woman in White* or *Dr Jekyll and Mr Hyde*.

The authors

Jane Austen (1775–1817) wrote a number of popular novels including *Northanger Abbey*. The best-known is probably *Pride and Prejudice* (1813) which has often been filmed and televised.

Charlotte and Emily Brontë. Charlotte (1816–55) published her best-known novel, *Jane Eyre*, under the male pseudonym Currer Bell. She wrote a number of other successful novels, including *Villette*. Her sister Emily (1818–48) used the pseudonym Ellis Bell for her only novel, *Wuthering Heights*. She was also a poet. Both sisters enjoyed an unusual amount of freedom as children due to their unconventional upbringing on the edge of the Yorkshire moors but suffered tragedy as tuberculosis brought early deaths to many of the family. Emily died shortly after the publication of her novel.

John Bunyan (1628–88), the son of a poor brazier, wrote *The Pilgrim's Progress* while in prison for his activities as a Nonconformist preacher. All his writings were strongly influenced by his religious beliefs.

Fanny Burney (1752–1840) wrote *Evelina* when she was in her early twenties. It was published anonymously but she greatly enjoyed the success of *Evelina* and her other novels when their authorship later became known.

Wilkie Collins (1824–89) was one of the first and most influential writers of the English 'mystery' novel. The most popular of his other novels is *The Moonstone* (1868).

Daniel Defoe (1660–1731) pursued a career as a merchant before he went bankrupt in 1692. He wrote many political pamphlets as well as novels such as *Robinson Crusoe*, *Moll Flanders* (1722) and *A Journal of the Plague Year* (1722).

Charles Dickens (1812–70) was one of the most popular authors of his time. Like Thackeray, the monthly appearances of his serialised novels became an eagerly awaited public event. Of all his novels, *David Copperfield* was his own personal favourite.

George Eliot (1819–80) was the pseudonym of Marian Evans. She grew up in the Midlands, the setting for her novel *The Mill on the Floss*. Her relationship with her brother Isaac bears certain similarities to the relationship between Maggie and Tom. Her most admired novel is *Middlemarch* (1871–2).

Henry Fielding (1707–54), called 'the father of the English novel' by Sir Walter Scott, started his literary career as a playwright. His first attempts at fiction were intended to be parodies of other novels but became popular in their own right.

Thomas Hardy (1840–1928). Most of Hardy's novels are set in the imaginary county of Wessex, based on Dorset where he spent most of his life. Some of his later novels, such as *Tess of the D'Urbervilles* (1891) and *Jude the Obscure* (1895), were controversial because of their unconventional approach to Victorian morality.

Samuel Richardson (1689–1761) was already a successful London printer when he wrote his first novel, *Pamela*, at the age of fifty. This was followed by other novels including *Clarissa* (1747–8) and *Sir Charles Grandison* (1753–4).

Laurence Sterne (1713–68), born in Ireland but educated at Cambridge, was a clergyman, amateur painter and musician as well as a writer. *Tristram Shandy* brought him both fame and criticism when it first appeared. More widely popular was his *A Sentimental Journey*, published in 1768, just before he died.

Robert Louis Stevenson (1850–94) was born in Edinburgh and was called to the Scottish Bar, although he never practised as a lawyer. He spent much of his life abroad because of frequent bouts of illness. His other works include *Kidnapped* (1886) and *A Child's Garden of Verses* (1885).

William Thackeray (1811–63) was driven to write *Vanity Fair* by the need for money. He received £60 per monthly part! The monthly appearances of his serial novels became part of English life.

Horace Walpole (1717–97) not only wrote a Gothic novel, *The Castle of Otranto*, but also built a Gothic mansion in Twickenham, near London, complete with turrets and cloisters. He was largely responsible for the Gothic 'craze' that followed.

Further reading

Pride and Prejudice (1813) by Jane Austen
Mrs Bennet is trying to find husbands for her five
daughters. In the characters of Mr Collins, Lady Catherine
de Bourgh and Mrs Bennet, Jane Austen has created some
memorable caricatures.

Frankenstein (1818) by Mary Shelley
In this well-known horror classic, the monster can be seen
as Dr Frankenstein's *alter ego*.

Jane Eyre (1847) by Charlotte Brontë
A 'Cinderella' story of a young girl's quest for happiness.

Barchester Towers (1857) by Anthony Trollope
A gallery of memorable characters living in a small,
closeknit community.

Great Expectations (1861) by Charles Dickens
A young boy's encounter with an escaped convict changes
the course of his life. An interesting comparison with *David
Copperfield* in its depiction of childhood.

Middlemarch (1871–2) by George Eliot
The ideals of a young doctor are put to test in the town of
Middlemarch. This novel is a powerful study of individuals
caught in a community.

Tess of the D'Urbervilles (1891) by Thomas Hardy
A sympathetic portrait of a young woman's struggles and
sufferings.

What Maisie Knew (1897) by Henry James
The adult world seen through a child's eyes.

The Catcher in the Rye (1951) by J.D. Salinger (Penguin, 1994)
Teenager Holden Caulfield takes a critical look at the world.

The Color Purple (1983) by Alice Walker (The Women's Press, 1992)
The story of a young Black girl forced into marriage in the Deep South, USA.

Oranges are Not the Only Fruit (1985) by Jeannette Winterson (Vintage, 1991)
Caricatures and comic characters enliven this story of a young girl growing up in a religious household.

Further reading projects

1 Make a study of the way any of these writers portray the experience of growing up.

2 Keep a reading diary of your reactions to the characters in one of the novels recommended here. Use your notes to write your own character study.

3 Compare the way different writers portray religious characters. Choose any of the range of vicars, priests, religious enthusiasts and holy men and women you will find in these books.

4 Choose any two of the young male characters from any of these novels and compare their experience of being young and male.

5 Choose a selection of female characters from novels from different centuries. Compare their experience of being female.

Longman Group Limited
Longman House, Burnt Mill, Harlow,
Essex CM20 2JE, England
and Associated Companies throughout the world.

This educational edition first published 1996

Editorial material set in 10/12.5 point Stone Sans
Produced by Longman Singapore Publishers (Pte) Ltd
Printed in Singapore

ISBN 0 582 25388 8

Cover illustration by John Brennan
Cover design by Ship

Cover illustration: Jekyll and Hyde

The publisher's policy is to use paper manufactured from sustainable
forests